the AMAZING SPIDER-MAN™

BIRTH OF VENOM

Reader Services

CUSTOMER SERVICE IN THE UK AND REPUBLIC OF IRELAND

How to continue your collection:
Customers can either place an order with their newsagent or receive issues on subscription.
Back issues: Either order through your newsagent or write to: Marvel Collection, Jacklin Enterprises UK, PO Box 77, Jarrow, NE32 3YH, enclosing payment of the cover price plus £1.00 p&p per copy. (Republic of Ireland: cover price plus €1.75).
Subscriptions: You can have your issues sent directly to your home. For details, see insert in issue 1 or phone our Customer Service Hotline on 0871 472 4240 (Monday to Friday, 9am-5pm, calls cost 10p per minute from UK landline). Alternatively you can write to Marvel Collection, Jacklin Enterprises UK, PO Box 77, Jarrow, NE32 3YH, or fax your enquiries to 0871 472 4241, or e-mail: marvelcollection@jacklinservice.com or visit www.graphicnovelcollection.com

CUSTOMER SERVICE IN OVERSEAS MARKETS

Australia: Back issues can be ordered from your newsagent. Alternatively telephone (03) 9872 4000 or write to:
Back Issues Department, Bissett Magazine Services, PO Box 3460, Nunawading Vic 3131. Please enclose payment of the cover price, plus A$2.49 (inc. GST) per issue postage and handling. Back issues are subject to availability.
Subscriptions: You can have your issues sent directly to your home. For details, see insert in issue 1 or phone our Customer Service Hotline on (03) 9872 4000. Alternatively you can write to Hachette subs offer, Bissett Magazine Services, PO Box 3460, Nunawading Vic 3131, or fax your enquiries to (03) 9873 4988, or order online at www.bissettmags.com.au

New Zealand: For back issues, ask your local magazine retailer or write to: Netlink, PO Box 47906, Ponsonby, Auckland.
South Africa: Back issues are available through your local CNA store or other newsagent.
Subscriptions: call (011) 265 4309, fax (011) 314 2984, or write to: Marvel Collection, Private Bag 10, Centurion 0046 or e-mail: service@jacklin.co.za
Malta: Back issues are only available through your local newsagent.
Malaysia: Call (03) 8023 3260, or e-mail: sales@allscript.com
Singapore: Call (65) 287 7090, or e-mail: sales@allscript.com

Published by Hachette Partworks Ltd, Jordan House, 47 Brunswick Place, London, N1 6EB
www.hachettepartworks.co.uk

Distributed in the UK and Republic of Ireland by Marketforce

This special edition published in 2012 by Hachette Partworks Ltd. forming part of The Ultimate Marvel Graphic Novel Collection.

Printed in China.
ISBN: 978-1-906965-91-4

Licensed by Marvel Characters B.V. through Panini S.p.A., Italy. All Rights Reserved.

TOM DEFALCO, LOUISE SIMONSON & DAVID MICHELINIE
WRITERS

RON FRENZ, GREG LAROCQUE & TODD MCFARLANE
PENCILS

JOSEF RUBINSTEIN, JIM MOONEY,
INKS

GLYNIS WEIN, CHRISTIE SCHEELE, BOB SHAREN & GEORGE
ROUSSOS
COLOURS

JOE ROSEN, JANICE CHIANG, RICK PARKER
LETTERS

DANNY FINGEROTH, JIM OWSLEY, JIM SALICRUP
EDITORS

JIM SHOOTER & TOM DEFALCO
EDITORS IN CHIEF

TODD MCFARLANE & AVALON'S ANDY TROY
COVER ART

SPIDER-MAN: BIRTH OF VENOM

Marco M. Lupoi
*Panini Publishing Director
(Europe)*

For years, comic fans had considered the Green Goblin to be Spider-Man's arch-nemesis, but in 1988, a new and even deadlier villain appeared to snatch that particular crown; a sadistic creature known simply as Venom. Hellbent on revenge and obsessed with killing the wall-crawler, he was an instant hit with readers.

You will have to forgive us if this seems a slightly condensed account of Venom's birth. We have included all the major twists and turns to his origin story, but in reality, we'd need a book ten times this size to tell the entire tale! From the black suit's first Earthbound appearance in Amazing Spider-Man #252 to the reveal of Venom in issue #300, the saga spanned over 50 issues. An evolving epic devised by multiple writers, building organically on the threads the other had left behind, and eventually leading to a monstrous foe unlike any Spider-Man had fought before.

It is also worth noting, that in the midst of this building tension we have one of the most moving issues of Spider-Man ever created, as Mary Jane reveals to Peter intimate details of her past. It is no easy thing for a writer to jump from outlandish stories about alien parasites and super-powered gang wars, to a tender episode of young lovers reconciling their differences, without seeming corny or radically out of place. Few fictional characters could get away with such a sudden shift in tone, but it is a testament to Spider-Man, and the Marvel Universe in general, that such a feat can be achieved so seamlessly.

So, read on, as the origin of Spider-Man's dark reflection is revealed!

"You may call me VENOM – For that's what I'm paid to spew out these days! I'm your victim Spider-Man – I'm the innocent you ruined! "

ntains material originally published in magazine form as THE AMAZING SPIDER-MAN #252, 256-259, 300 & WEB OF SPIDER-MAN #1 Senior Editor (Hachette Partworks Ltd.), Sarah Gale. Packag
Panini Publishing, a division of Panini UK Limited. Mike Riddell, Managing Director. Alan O'Keefe, Managing Editor. Ed Hammond, Editor. Marco M. Lupoi, Publishing Director Europe.
m Warran-Smith, Designer. Additional content: Rich Johnston. Office of publication: Brockbourne House, 77 Mount Ephraim, Tunbridge Wells, Kent TN4 8BS. No similarity between any of the names,
aracters, persons and/or institutions in this edition with those of any living or dead person or institution is intended, and any such similarity which may exist is purely coincidental. This publication may
old, except by authorised dealers, and is sold subject to the condition that it shall not be sold or distributed with any part of its cover or markings removed, nor in a mutilated condition

After rejecting his marriage proposal, Mary Jane leaves Peter Parker and moves to Florida. He starts a relationship with the reformed burglar the Black Cat and eventually reveals his secret identity to her. But the Black Cat has a secret of her own. She recently discovered that the man behind the process that augmented her bad luck powers was none other than the sinister crime boss, the Kingpin.

However, their relationship is put on hold when Spider-Man, along with a group of Earth's most famous Super Heroes and Villains are transported across the Universe to a planet called Battleworld. Once there, they are forced to take part in a conflict known as the Secret Wars. During the campaign, Spider-Man's original red and blue costume is destroyed. Luckily, he finds a piece of alien technology that creates what he thinks is a new black costume. Spidey is amazed to discover that his new costume responds to his thoughts, changing appearance at will and even creating its own organic supply of webbing.

As the Secret Wars come to an end, back on Earth, the general public continue to wonder what has happened to all the Heroes and if they will ever return...

MARVEL®

60¢
252
MAY
02457

APPROVED BY THE
COMICS CODE
AUTHORITY

TM

the AMAZING SPIDER-MAN®

SPIDER-MAN!

FRENZ
JANSON

THE PAPER LOOKS GOOD, ROBBIE-- **REAL GOOD!**

THIS LEAD STORY WILL HAVE EVERY-ONE IN THE CITY WONDERING WHAT'S HAPPENED TO THOSE HEROES.

I'M GLAD YOU'RE PLEASED, JONAH.

I HAVE ONLY ONE COMPLAINT...

YOU NEVER ONCE CONFRONTED THE QUESTION OF **SPIDER-MAN'S** INVOLVEMENT!

IS HE BEHIND THESE DISAPPEAR-ANCES? WHAT DOES HE HOPE TO GAIN?

SLOW DOWN, JONAH...

AS THE PUBLISHER OF THE **DAILY BUGLE,** YOU CAN REPLACE ME ANY TIME YOU CHOOSE, BUT AS LONG AS I'M THE EDITOR-IN-CHIEF HERE--

--I'M GOING TO RUN THIS NEWSPAPER **MY** WAY!

IF YOU WANT TO KEEP PERSECUT-ING SPIDER-MAN, YOU'LL HAVE TO DO IT ON THE EDITORIAL PAGES-- AND NOT IN MY HEADLINES!

IS THAT UNDERSTOOD?

¿HARUMPHH! I STILL WONDER HOW SPIDER-MAN'S MIXED UP IN ALL OF THIS!

SO DO I. I WISH I KNEW HOW ALL THE MISSING HEROES FIGURED IN...

THEY'VE BEEN GONE FOR DAYS!

MEANWHILE, IN THE **SHEEP MEADOW** OF NEW YORK'S CENTRAL PARK, THE POLICE HAVE CORDONED OFF THE AREA THAT ONCE HELD THE MYSTERIOUS STONEHENGELIKE CONSTRUCTION--

--WHICH TRANSPORTED THE VANISHED HEROES TO A GALAXY FAR BEYOND OUR OWN!

SUDDENLY, AN INCREDIBLE BURST OF BLINDING LIGHT SEEMS TO EXPLODE FROM WITHIN THE BARRICADES, AND THEN--

LOOK!

THAT'S THE THING WHICH KIDNAPPED THE HEROES! **IT'S BACK!** HOW--? WHY--?!

3

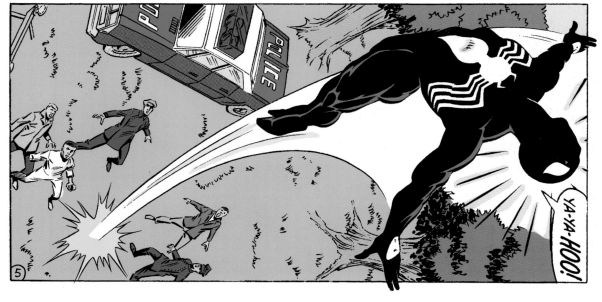

WE'RE BACK! *WE'RE BACK!*

HEY, *YOU!*

DO YOU MIND TELLING US WHAT'S GOING ON HERE?

WHO ARE YOU, ANYWAY?!

ME?! I'M SPIDER-MAN--

--AND I'M REAL GLAD TO KNOW YOU!

SMEK!

⸮?!?⸮

CUT THE COMEDY, WISE GUY!

WE'VE ALL SEEN SPIDER-MAN BEFORE-- AND YOU DON'T LOOK A THING LIKE HIM!

WE WANT SOME ANSWERS-- *NOW!*

BE CAREFUL WITH THAT GUN, QUICKDRAW!

WE DON'T WANT IT TO ACCIDENTALLY GO OFF, AND HURT SOMEONE--

PWIP!

"--DO WE?!"

MY HAND--?

WHAT DID HE DO TO MY HAND?

AT THAT EXACT INSTANT, THE BIZARRE CONSTRUCT FLARES AGAIN, AND THEN...

HEY! LOOK WHO DECIDED TO JOIN THE PARTY!

THE *AVENGERS!*

⸮WHEW⸮ IT'S ABOUT TIME! FOR A MINUTE THERE, I WAS AFRAID THAT CONNORS AND I WERE THE ONLY ONES WHO MADE IT HOME!

6

SOON, NEAR THE EDGE OF THE PARK, SPIDER-MAN PLACES DR. CURT CONNORS UPON THE GROUND, AND THEN LEAPS UPWARD AGAIN...

WHAT IS IT, SPIDER-MAN?

WHAT ARE YOU LOOKING FOR UP THERE?

MY CLOTHES!

I HID MY CIVIES IN ONE OF THESE TREES--JUST MINUTES BEFORE I GOT WHISKED AWAY TO THAT OTHER GALAXY! *

OH, NO!

* SEE LAST ISSUE--DANNY.

MY NEW JACKET AND MY SHOES MUST HAVE FALLEN TO THE GROUND WHEN MY WEB-BALL EVAPORATED! THEY'RE GONE--AND SOME BIRD CONVERTED THE REST OF MY CLOTHES INTO THE SUPERSTRUCTURE FOR HIS NEW NEST!

≶UGGG≶ WHAT A MESS! I'LL NEVER BE ABLE TO WEAR THEM AGAIN!

AT LEAST MY WALLET AND KEYS ARE STILL HERE!

GUESS IT'S TIME TO SEE IF MY NEW COSTUME STILL WORKS LIKE IT DID ON THAT OTHER PLANET!

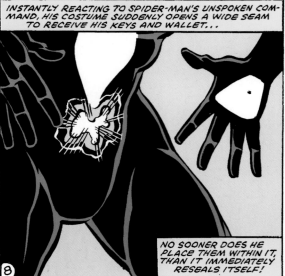

INSTANTLY REACTING TO SPIDER-MAN'S UNSPOKEN COMMAND, HIS COSTUME SUDDENLY OPENS A WIDE SEAM TO RECEIVE HIS KEYS AND WALLET...

NO SOONER DOES HE PLACE THEM WITHIN IT, THAN IT IMMEDIATELY RESEALS ITSELF!

WOW! I DON'T THINK I'LL EVER GET USED TO THAT STUNT!

THIS COSTUME POSSESSES SOME PRETTY WEIRD ABILITIES! I'M REALLY GOING TO NEED TIME TO ADJUST TO THEM!

HEADS UP, DOCTOR CONNORS! I'M COMING BACK FOR YOU NOW!

8

SHORTLY... HANG ON, DOC! I'LL HAVE YOU HOME BEFORE YOU KNOW IT!

JUST A FEW MORE BLOCKS UNTIL WE REACH YOUR APARTMENT!

MADE IT!

HI THERE, BILLY! BET YOU DIDN'T EXPECT TO FIND US HANGING ON THE SIDE OF YOUR BUILDING!

DAD!

TAP! TAP!

MOMENTS LATER...

MOM AND I WERE SO WORRIED! WE WERE AFRAID THAT,.. THAT...

THAT I HAD AGAIN BEEN TRANSFORMED INTO THAT MINDLESS, RAMPAGING BEAST-- THE LIZARD?!

DON'T WORRY, SON! EVERYTHING IS ALL RIGHT NOW!

CURTIS! YOU'RE HOME! YOU'RE SAFE!

NOT WISHING TO INTRUDE ON THIS MOST TENDER OF FAMILY REUNIONS, SPIDER-MAN QUIETLY TAKES HIS LEAVE...

WHERE WERE YOU? WHY DIDN'T YOU CALL?

LISTEN, I'M NOT SURE I UNDERSTAND WHERE I WAS... OR ALL THAT HAPPENED TO ME WHILE I WAS AWAY...

...I JUST KNOW I'M GLAD THAT SPIDER-MAN WAS THERE TO HELP ME THROUGH IT!

THAT WAS SPIDER-MAN?! GOSH, I DIDN'T EVEN RECOGNIZE HIM!

WHAT HAPPENED? DID HE GET A NEW TAILOR?

NO... NOT QUITE.

I DON'T KNOW WHAT THE FUTURE HOLDS FOR CURT CONNORS-- BUT I WISH HIM THE BEST! HE AND HIS FAMILY HAVE BEEN THROUGH ENOUGH GRIEF IN THE PAST FEW YEARS!

9

CAN IT BE?! DO MY EYES DECEIVE ME?

IS THIS REALLY THE BATHROOM SKYLIGHT WHICH OPENS TO THE HOME OF THAT CELEBRATED, WORLD-FAMOUS, GALAXY-HOPPING FREELANCE PHOTOGRAPHER... *PETER PARKER?!*

SO IT IS! SO IT IS!

÷GNUU÷ THIS ROOM HAS A DESPERATE NEED FOR AIR FRESHENER!

A *CASE* AT THE VERY LEAST!

THERE WERE SOME BAD MOMENTS IN THE LAST FEW DAYS, WHEN I WAS CONVINCED I'D NEVER SEE THIS OLD HOMESTEAD AGAIN--

--LIKE THAT TIME *GALACTUS* ALMOST STEPPED ON ME!

OH, WELL, I...

HEY!

THE COSTUME IS RESPONDING TO MY THOUGHTS AGAIN!

IT KNEW THAT I WANTED TO CHANGE BACK TO PETER PARKER--SO IT TRANSFORMED ITS OUTWARD APPEARANCE!

WEIRD! IT TREATS MY EVERY THOUGHT AS A COMMAND!

REED RICHARDS VOLUNTEERED TO ANALYZE IT FOR ME! MAYBE I'LL TAKE HIM UP ON HIS OFFER--

--AFTER I'VE SEEN TO A FEW PROBLEMS OF A FAR MORE PERSONAL NATURE!

MY FACE HASN'T SEEN A RAZOR IN DAYS...

"DAYS"?!

OMIGOSH! I HAVEN'T SPOKEN TO AUNT MAY IN OVER A WEEK!

SHE MUST BE WORRIED SICK!

AND, A FRANTIC DIAL LATER...

10

PETER? IT SEEMS LIKE IT'S BEEN AGES SINCE YOU LAST CALLED! WHEREVER HAVE YOU BEEN KEEPING YOURSELF?

LEAVE THE BOY ALONE, MAY! STOP TRYING TO SMOTHER HIM!

I'M SORRY, AUNT MAY! I WAS, UH, CALLED OUT OF TOWN UNEXPEC-TEDLY... ON A PHOTO ASSIGN-MENT!

I INTENDED TO STOP BY FOR A VISIT BEFORE I LEFT, BUT I JUST DIDN'T GET THE CHANCE!

YES...YES...OF COURSE I FORGIVE YOU...IT'S JUST THAT YOU KNOW HOW I SOMETIMES WORRY WHEN I DON'T HEAR FROM YOU!

"SOMETIMES WORRY"?! MAY PARKER, YOU HAVE THE MOST INCREDIBLE GIFT FOR UNDERSTATE-MENT!...AND ALL WITH A STRAIGHT FACE, TOO!

HUSH, NATHAN! PETER'S TALKING...

THAT'S ALL RIGHT, AUNT MAY! I'D HATE TO INTERRUPT A MASTER SHOW-MAN WHEN HE'S ON A ROLL!

SUNDAY DINNER?! I'D LOVE TO JOIN YOU AND NATHAN... BUT ONLY IF I CAN BRING THE DESSERT!

WELL, THEN YOU CAN EXPECT ME!

IT USED TO BE, IF I WAS OUT OF TOUCH, AUNT MAY WOULD FLIP! SHE SEEMS SO TOGETHER THESE DAYS! I GUESS MOST OF THAT IS NATHAN LUBENSKY'S DOING! HE'S BEEN MIGHTY GOOD FOR HER!

I'VE GOT ANOTHER IMPORTANT PHONE CALL TO MAKE!

THIS ONE'S TO MY LADY--

"--FELICIA HARDY, THE BLACK CAT!"

BRRING! BRRING! BRRING!

NO ANSWER! I WONDER WHERE SHE COULD BE?

FELICIA AND I HAVE SOME SERIOUS TALKING TO DO!

I'M GETTING BETTER AND BETTE
BURMA SH

IT'S TIME WE STRAIGHTENED OUT THIS WACKY RELATIONSHIP OF OURS!

11

I KNOW THAT SOMETHING HAS BEEN TROUBLING HER LATELY-- BUT SHE WON'T LET ME IN ON IT!

WHAT CAN IT BE?

WHY WON'T SHE CONFIDE IN ME?!

ACCORDING TO CAPTAIN AMERICA AND THE HUMAN TORCH, SHE'S BEEN RACING AROUND TOWN-- TRYING TO FIND A WAY TO ACQUIRE SUPER-POWERS*...

...SO SHE CAN BATTLE BY MY SIDE!

THE LADY'S ASKING FOR TROUBLE... BUT SHE'S SO HEAD-STRONG...

* SEE PETER PARKER, THE SPECTACULAR SPIDER-MAN #89 -- DANNY.

BUT WHY COMPLAIN? I REALLY CARE FOR HER-- EVEN THOUGH SHE CAN BE SO FLAKEY AT TIMES!

I'LL TRY TO REACH HER AGAIN LATER-- AFTER I'VE HAD A CHANCE TO CHOW DOWN!

RIGHT NOW, MY BODY CRAVES FOOD! TRAVELING ACROSS THE UNIVERSE IS HUNGRY WORK!

BUT THEN, MINUTES AFTER PETER PARKER HAS QUIT HIS APARTMENT--

-- A SHAPELY SILHOUETTE STEALS ACROSS HIS BATHROOM SKYLIGHT!

MOVING WITH THE SUBTLE GRACE OF HER NAMESAKE, THE BLACK CAT GENTLY DROPS INTO THE APARTMENT...

SHE IS A REFORMED CAT BURGLAR, GIFTED WITH INCREDIBLE PHYSICAL AGILITY.

SPIDER--?

HE DOESN'T SEEM TO BE HOME!

SHE IS ALSO A WOMAN VERY MUCH IN LOVE WITH THE AMAZING SPIDER-MAN.

HE'S BEEN GONE FOR DAYS! WHERE CAN HE BE? WHY HASN'T HE TRIED TO CONTACT ME?

WHY DOES HE HAVE TO BE GONE NOW-- WHEN I NEED HIM THE MOST?!

I'VE GOT REAL PROBLEMS! I WANTED TO BE THE PERFECT PARTNER FOR MY SPIDER-- SO I LET SOME SCIENCE BOYS CONDUCT A FEW EXPERIMENTS ON ME!

THEY MANAGED TO RELEASE -- AND ENHANCE-- SOME PRETTY FUNKY LATENT SUPER-POWERS THAT I NEVER REALIZED I HAD!

BUT THEN, I LEARNED THAT THE MAN RESPONSIBLE FOR MY TRANSFORMATION WAS ONE OF SPIDER'S GREATEST ENEMIES...THE KINGPIN OF CRIME!

12

MINUTES LATER...

I'M CERTAIN THE KINGPIN HAS SOMETHING SINISTER UP HIS OVERSIZED SLEEVE!

HE MIGHT EVEN THINK HE CAN USE *ME* AGAINST SPIDER-MAN -- BUT HE'S WRONG!

STILL, JUST TO BE SAFE, I'D LIKE TO FIND SPIDER-- AND WARN HIM!

WHERE *IS* HE?!

PIZZA-- THE SUSTENANCE OF THE GODS!

SMELL THAT AROMA! I HOPE MARIO REMEMBERED TO USE EXTRA GREEN PEPPERS AND ANCHOVIES!

IT'S AMAZING WHAT YOU MISS-- WHEN YOU'RE A MILLION-ZILLION MILES FROM HOME!

TOMORROW, I'M HAVING TACOS FOR LUNCH-- AND CHINESE FOR DINNER!

MAN! I'M SO GLAD TO BE BACK!

EVERYTHING LOOKS GREAT TO ME-- EVEN THE BUMS ON THE STREET...AND THIS GRIMY, OLD STOOP!

HEY, LOOKEE HERE!

I EVEN HAVE SOME MAIL WAITING FOR ME!

JUST A FEW BILLS AND ADVERTISEMENTS-- BUT I DON'T CARE! IT'S ALL A PART OF BEING HOME!

SALE

13

SHORTLY...

THEY MAY NOT BE COSMIC PROBLEMS-- BUT MY RENT'S COMING DUE IN A FEW DAYS.... AND I'VE GOT OTHER BILLS TO PAY!

I COULD REALLY USE SOME BIG BUCKS!

HEY, I WONDER IF--

MY CAMERA!

MY COSTUME MUST HAVE KNOWN THAT I WANTED IT!

POP

GOSH, I HAD EVEN FORGOTTEN THAT THIS CAMERA WAS STILL INSIDE THE COSTUME WHEN IT CHANGED ITS APPEARANCE!

I REALLY DO HAVE TO GIVE REED RICHARDS A VISIT-- AND SOON!

BUT NOW--

"-- I'VE GOT SOME FILM TO DEVELOP!"

I MANAGED TO SNAP QUITE A FEW PIX OF THAT ALIEN ADVENTURE --

-- BEFORE I RAN OUT OF FILM!

WOW! I KNEW THESE PICTURES WERE WEIRD WHEN I TOOK THEM-- BUT I HAD NO IDEA HOW WEIRD!

BEAUTIFUL ...AND YET, SO VERY TERRIFYING!

I'LL BET I COULD MAKE A SMALL FORTUNE SELLING THESE TO THE NEWS MAGAZINES!

14

YEAH...A FORTUNE!

OH, WHO AM I TRYING TO KID?!

EVERYONE WILL THINK THESE PICTURES WERE FAKED!

BESIDES, REED RICHARDS WAS RIGHT!

WE SHOULDN'T BURDEN THE PUBLIC WITH WHAT HAPPENED TO US OUT THERE!

NO ONE SHOULD HAVE TO LIVE WITH KNOWLEDGE LIKE THAT...

...NOT EVEN ME!

I'M GONNA DESTROY THE PRINTS *AND* THE NEGATIVES!

WITHIN MINUTES, IT IS DONE...

AND...

≈YAWN≈ THAT'S IT! I'VE HAD MORE THAN ENOUGH FOR ONE DAY!

IT'S TIME TO CRASH!

SLEEP, HOWEVER, REFUSES TO COME.

FOR MORE THAN AN HOUR PETER PARKER TOSSES WITHIN HIS BED--

--BUT MORPHEUS STEADFASTLY REFUSES TO EMBRACE HIM!

15

17

BUT SOON, WHILE SWINGING HIGH OVER A VACANT LOT, SPIDER-MAN'S JUBILATION IS SUDDENLY SHATTERED BY THE HARSH SHOUTS OF ANGRY VOICES...

SOUNDS LIKE MORE TROUBLE DOWN THERE!

SHUT UP, WEEZIE! I'M WARNING YOU--!

NO! YOU LIED TO ME, JUSTIN! YOU MADE A PROMISE TO ME, AND YOU LIED!

THAT DOES IT! IF YOU WON'T CLOSE YOUR MOUTH --I WILL!

SLOW DOWN, CHAMP!

DIDN'T YOUR MOTHER EVER TEACH YOU THAT GENTLEMEN DO NOT SLUG LADIES?

÷ULP÷

WHAT ARE YOU KIDS DOING OUT SO LATE?

AND WHAT WERE YOU FIGHTING ABOUT?

IT'S, UM, ALL JUSTIN'S FAULT!

NO, IT AIN'T!

IT IS SO! HE PROMISED TO TAKE ME TO A CONCERT TONIGHT-- BUT HE BACKED OUT AT THE LAST MINUTE!

THAT'S IT?! YOU'RE FIGHTING OVER A DATE?!

I WAS COUNTING ON THIS CONCERT! IT WAS MY FAVORITE GROUP... BURNT TOAST!

IT AIN'T MY FAULT I COULDN'T GET TICKETS!

BESIDES, I THINK THEY'RE PRETTY LAME-O, ANYWAY!

ENOUGH! TAKE A BREATHER, KIDS! YOU'RE BOTH BEHAVING LIKE IDIOTS!

IT'S STUPID FOR YOU TO BE FIGHTING-- ESPECIALLY WHEN YOU HAVE SO MUCH GOING FOR YOU!

18

--WHEREVER YOU GO!

THAT'S WHAT YOU'VE GOT GOING FOR YOU! IT'S A LOT MORE THAN YOU THINK!

MINUTES LATER...

THANKS FOR THE RIDE, MISTER! I KNOW JUSTIN REALLY HATED IT--

--BUT I HAD A GOOD TIME!

SO DID I!

YOU KNOW SOMETHING, MISTER? YOU'RE A NICE GUY...BUT AWFUL WEIRD!

I GUESS I AM AT THAT!

WEIRDER THAN SOME...BUT NOT AS WEIRD AS OTHERS!

THEN I DON'T WANT TO MEET THE OTHERS!

NEITHER DID I... BUT I DIDN'T HAVE ANY CHOICE!

GOOD-BYE, WEEZIE! HAVE A GOOD LIFE!

MAN! I DON'T KNOW IF THAT DID MORE GOOD FOR THEM-- OR ME!

BUT I FEEL EVEN BETTER THAN I DID BEFORE!

NEW YORK, YOU REALLY KNOW HOW TO BRING OUT THE VERY BEST IN--

2

MEANWHILE, IN THE RAFTERS...

KLIK! WHRR!

HER REAL NAME IS FELICIA HARDY. HOWEVER, SHE PREFERS TO BE KNOWN AS...THE *BLACK CAT!*

POSSESSING THE SPEED, GRACE AND AGILITY OF HER COLORFUL NAMESAKE, SHE IS THE TRUE LOVE AND SOMETIME PARTNER OF THE EVER-SPECTACULAR SPIDER-MAN...

RECENTLY,* THANKS TO THE KINGPIN OF CRIME, SHE GAINED ADDITIONAL POWER, POWER SHE DOES NOT YET UNDERSTAND OR CONTROL--

KLIK! WHRR!

-- WHICH ALTERS PROBABILITY TO CAUSE *BAD LUCK* TO STRIKE ANYONE WHO ATTEMPTS TO HARM HER!

*SEE SPECTACULAR SPIDER-MAN #89 FOR DETAILS -- DANNY.

SHE KEEPS THIS LAST POWER A CLOSELY GUARDED SECRET. EVEN FROM THE MAN SHE LOVES...

OH, SPIDER...

...I KNOW YOU SUPPORT YOURSELF BY SELLING PICTURES LIKE THESE TO THE DAILY BUGLE--

KLIK! WHRR!

"--BUT I WISH YOU WOULDN'T HOG ALL THE *FUN*--

"--FOR YOURSELF!"

KA-VWAM!

3

5

--THAT'S THE *LEAST* OF YOUR PROBLEMS!

¿UNNN?

PWAM!

FELICIA REALLY LACED INTO THAT KID, BUT HE DESERVED IT! SHE COULD HAVE BEEN SERIOUSLY HURT, IF HIS GUN HADN'T MISFIRED!

I WISH SHE'D BE MORE CAREFUL! SHE KNOWS THAT I DON'T APPROVE OF THE WAY SHE RISKS HER LIFE FIGHTING BY MY SIDE, BUT SHE JUST WON'T LISTEN TO REASON!

SPRAYING THE MEN WITH HIS SUPER-ADHESIVE WEBBING, SPIDER-MAN LEAVES THEM FOR THE POLICE...

RWIP

RWIP

MINUTES LATER...

SPIDER, YOU HAVEN'T SAID A WORD SINCE WE LEFT THE WAREHOUSE. IS SOMETHING BOTHERING YOU?

IT'S NOTHING NEW, CAT...

IT'S JUST THAT I THINK YOU'RE TOO FOOLHARDY! YOU TAKE TOO MANY NEEDLESS CHANCES!

LOOK WHO'S TALKING--!

IT'S DIFFERENT FOR ME! I HAVE *REAL* SUPER POWERS--

--PLUS A *SPIDER-SENSE* WHICH WARNS ME OF DANGER! YOU'RE ONLY A HIGHLY TRAINED GYMNAST!

ONLY--?! HEY, I APPRECIATE YOUR CONCERN --IT'S REAL SWEET-- BUT IT ISN'T NECESSARY!

THIS IS ONE CAT WHO KNOWS HOW TO LAND ON HER FEET!

I HOPE SO...

LIGHTEN UP, LOVER!

I WANT TO PARTY!

I HATE TO DISAPPOINT YOU, KID--

--BUT I'M MAKING THIS AN EARLY NIGHT!

I'VE GOTTA GET HOME, AND DEVELOP THESE PICTURES BEFORE MORNING.

OH, POO! YOU CAN BE SUCH A SPOILSPORT AT TIMES-- BUT I KNOW BETTER THAN TO ARGUE WHEN YOU'VE GOT WORK TO DO.

GUESS I'LL JUST HAVE TO SETTLE FOR A GOODNIGHT KISS, INSTEAD.

TRIGGERED BY SPIDER-MAN'S THOUGHTS, HIS COSTUME--AN AMAZING SOUVENIR FROM A DISTANT PLANET--IMMEDIATELY OPENS A WIDE SEAM AROUND HIS MOUTH, AS ONE KISS TURNS TO MANY...

AND THEN...

POOR SPIDER! I'D LOVE TO TELL HIM ABOUT MY ENHANCED ATHLETIC PROWESS, AND MY BAD LUCK POWERS--

--BUT HE'D BE IN A REAL PANIC IF HE EVER LEARNED THAT I GOT THEM FROM HIS ENEMY-- THE KINGPIN!

6

SOMETIME LATER, AS SPIDER-MAN RETURNS TO HIS CHELSEA APARTMENT...

I MUST BE CRAZY!

ONLY A FIRST CLASS NUT WOULD GIVE UP A CHANCE TO GO MESSING AROUND THE ROOFTOPS WITH THE BLACK CAT!

THE DAILY BUGLE COULDN'T POSSIBLY PAY ME ENOUGH FOR THESE PIX TO BE WORTH THAT KIND OF SACRIFICE--!

OH, WELL, NO ONE EVER SAID THAT THE LIFE OF A FREELANCE PHOTOHOUND WOULD BE EASY--

-- AND IT'S NOT!

A MENTAL COMMAND CAUSES HIS COSTUME TO MELT AWAY FROM HIS HANDS AND FACE...

-YAWN- I'M REALLY WRECKED TONIGHT-- BUT THAT SEEMS TO BE THE GENERAL RULE THESE DAYS. I NEVER SEEM TO GET ENOUGH SLEEP. I'M ALWAYS TIRED!

I'D BETTER GET COOKING ON THOSE PHOTOS BEFORE I COMPLETELY FALL OUT...

AND SO...

GOT TO GIVE THE CAT CREDIT-- SHE KNOWS HOW TO HANDLE A CAMERA!

THESE ARE GOOD! REAL GOOD!

WISH I COULD SAY THAT I'M THRILLED, BUT I'M NOT! IT'S REAL OBVIOUS THAT SHE TAKES A MUCH BETTER PICTURE THAN I DO.

THAT BOTHERS ME! A LOT!

IT'S TIME I TOOK THIS WORK A BIT MORE SERIOUSLY!

MAYBE I SHOULD TAKE A FEW COURSES TO IMPROVE MY SKILLS!

AFTER SELECTING THE VERY BEST PHOTOS, HE TURNS TO STORE THE OTHERS AWAY--

-- BUT THEN...

OH, NO!

OF ALL THE CLUMSY--!

WHAT'S WRONG WITH ME LATELY? I SEEM TO BE ALL THUMBS!

I WONDER IF IT'S TIED IN WITH MY GENERAL LETHARGY?

GEE, I HOPE I'M NOT COMING DOWN WITH ANYTHING!

HEY! IN THE CORNER--!

MY OLD, SPARE COSTUME!

7

GOSH, I HAD FORGOTTEN ALL ABOUT THIS OLD THING!

I USED IT FOR A BACK-UP WHENEVER MY MAIN COSTUME NEEDED CLEANING OR REPAIRS. JUST SEEING IT AGAIN BRINGS BACK MEMORIES...

WHEN I DESIGNED MY VERY FIRST SPIDER-MAN COSTUME, I WAS LOOKING TO STRIKE IT BIG IN SHOW BUSINESS! I WANTED SOMETHING FLASHY! COLORFUL!

OVER THE YEARS, IT CAME TO MEAN...TO SYMBOLIZE...SO MUCH MORE TO ME!

BUT, EVEN SO, IT COULDN'T DO STUNTS LIKE THIS--!

"I STILL HAVE TROUBLE BELIEVING THAT THIS NEW COSTUME CAME FROM A WORLD AT THE OTHER END OF THE UNIVERSE.*

*SEE THE MARVEL SUPER HEROES SECRET WARS LIMITED SERIES FOR DETAILS -- DANNY!

"IT'S REALLY WEIRD TO HAVE A PIECE OF CLOTHING WHICH OBEYS MY MENTAL COMMANDS --AND ASSUMES ANY APPEAR-ANCE I IMAGINE!

"I GUESS I COULD MAKE IT LOOK LIKE MY OLD, FAMILIAR RED AND BLUE THREADS--"

--BUT, THAT WOULDN'T SEEM RIGHT!

NO, IT'S TIME TO PUT THE PAST BEHIND ME!

I'VE GROWN OLDER AND, HOPEFULLY, WISER IN THE LAST FEW YEARS...

...MAYBE MY NEW LOOK WILL HELP REFLECT THOSE CHANGES!

≷YAWN≷ ENOUGH DIME STORE PHILOSOPHY FOR ONE NIGHT!

IT'S TIME TO HIT THE SHEETS!

8

BUT THEN, EVEN AS PETER PARKER DRIFTS INTO THE REALM OF DREAMS--

--HIS ALIEN COSTUME SEEMINGLY SPRINGS TO LIFE!

FLOWING ACROSS THE FLOOR, IT SILENTLY ADVANCES ON THE SLEEPING ADVENTURER...

AS IF CONTEMPLATING THE HORRIBLE CONSEQUENCES OF ITS NEXT ACTION, IT PAUSES FOR ONE BRIEF MOMENT...

AND THEN--

--IT STRIKES!

SOMETIME LATER...

SHOVE OFF, PRINCE! I'M CLAIMING THAT REFRIGERATOR CRATE FOR MYSELF!

I BEG TO DIFFER, BABYFACE.

SINCE I'M THE ONE WHO FOUND IT, IT'S ONLY FAIR THAT I GET TO SLEEP IN IT.

NOBODY CARES ABOUT "FAIR" IN THE REAL WORLD!

IT'S EVERY MAN FOR HIMSELF!

HEY--!

WHO...WHAT...IS THAT--?!

I...DUNNO.

Y'KNOW SOMETHING, BABYFACE? I THINK THIS CRATE COULD ACCOMMODATE THE TWO OF US!

I HOPE SO, MAN! AFTER SEEING THAT...THAT THING PROWLING AROUND, I COULD USE SOME COMPANY!

ME, TOO!

9

EARLY THE NEXT MORNING...

BOSS--! OUR MAIN WAREHOUSE WAS RAIDED LAST NIGHT BY SPIDER-MAN AND THE POLICE!

OUR LAWYER THINKS HE CAN GET OUR PEOPLE BACK ON THE STREETS BY LATE AFTERNOON--

--BUT IT'LL STILL TAKE A FEW WEEKS BEFORE OUR FENCING OPERATION IS ROLLING AT FULL CAPACITY AGAIN!

THE LOSS IN REVENUE WILL BE SIGNIFICANT.

A PITY.

SNIPP!

HOWEVER, SPIDER-MAN IS THE MORE DISTRESSING PROBLEM.

THIS IS THE SECOND TIME HE'S INTERFERED IN THE ROSE'S AFFAIRS. I WON'T TOLERATE A THIRD.

HE MUST BE ELIMINATED ...AT ONCE!

IS THAT WISE, ROSE?

I THOUGHT THE KINGPIN HAD TO SANCTION ALL HITS THAT BIG!

MR. JOHNSTON, I REPORT TO THE KINGPIN OF CRIME JUST AS YOU AND MR. VARLEY REPORT TO ME...BUT, IN THIS ONE INSTANCE, I DO NOT HAVE TIME FOR THE LUXURY OF GOING THROUGH THE PROPER CHANNELS.

SPIDER-MAN IS A WEED WHICH MUST BE SWIFTLY PLUCKED.

I WANT HIM DEAD!

AND, I KNOW JUST THE MAN FOR THE JOB...

10

HEARTSDALE, NEW MEXICO...

A SMALL, BUT GROWING CITY--

--WHICH HOUSES THE CORPORATE HEADQUARTERS OF *FIREHEART ENTERPRISES*...

WHERE IS HE?

WE'RE DUE AT THE MAYOR'S OFFICE IN FIFTEEN MINUTES!

I'M AFRAID THAT MR. FIREHEART IS UNABLE TO ATTEND THAT MEETING, CONGRESSMAN.

HE WAS CALLED AWAY RATHER UNEXPECTEDLY THIS MORNING.

WHAT?!

HE ASKED ME TO CONVEY HIS SINCEREST APOLOGIES.

B-BUT WE WERE SUPPOSED TO DISCUSS THOSE NEW SHOPPING MALLS HE PLANS TO BUILD! WHAT SHOULD I TELL THE ZONING COMMISSION? THE CITY COUNCIL--?!

I DON'T KNOW CONGRESSMAN. I'LL HAVE MR. FIREHEART PHONE YOU AS SOON AS HE RETURNS.

B-ZIT

A CALL ON THOMAS'S PRIVATE LINE--!

11

YOU'LL HAVE TO EXCUSE ME, CONGRESSMAN, I HAVE OTHER WORK TO DO.

WITHOUT ANOTHER WORD, *JENNA TAYLOR* ENTERS THE PRIVATE OFFICE OF HER EMPLOYER--

-- THE MYSTERIOUS THOMAS FIREHEART!

I FEEL BADLY FOR CONGRESSMAN CRESPI. THOSE SHOPPING MALLS MEAN A LOT TO HIM--AND THE COMMUNITY! THIS IS ONE MEETING THOMAS SHOULDN'T HAVE MISSED.

OH, WELL, IT'S NOT MY PLACE TO CRITICIZE THE BOSS. I'M ONLY HIS EXECUTIVE ASSISTANT-- NOT HIS WIFE!

I GET THE FUN JOBS-- LIKE TELLING CRESPI THE BAD NEWS, AND ACTIVATING THIS CRAZY TELEPHONE GIZMO--

-- WHENEVER THOMAS ISN'T AROUND TO ANSWER HIS PRIVATE LINE.

KLIK!

MNNN

PLEASE LEAVE YOUR MESSAGE...

MNNN

"...AT THE SOUND OF THE *BEEP*."

THAT HUM--! IT'S PROBABLY FROM AN ELECTRONIC SCRAMBLING DEVICE WHICH PROTECTS HIS LINE FROM TAPS!

THIS IS THE ROSE...

I NEED YOU.

HHM! THAT WAS SHORT, AND TO THE POINT.

"THE ROSE"?! I DON'T RECOGNIZE THE NAME, BUT IT SOUNDED LIKE THOMAS WILL WANT TO KNOW ABOUT THIS CALL....AND FAST!

KLIK!

JENNA DEPRESSES ANOTHER BUTTON--

--AND, SIXTY MILES AWAY...

BLEEP! BLEEP!

BLEEP! BLEEP!

12

MEANWHILE, SEVERAL HUNDRED YARDS FROM THE HELICOPTER, A MANLIKE FIGURE RACES ALONG THE UNEVEN GROUND.

WITH PHYSICAL SENSES WHICH HAVE BEEN HEIGHTENED TO SUPER HUMAN LEVELS--

--HE FOLLOWS A SPOOR THAT WOULD BE TOTALLY INVISIBLE TO MOST HUMAN TRACKERS!

THEY DON'T KNOW IT YET-- BUT THEY'RE GOING TO DIE FOR WHAT THEY DID LAST NIGHT!

IT'S THEIR OWN FAULT! THEY SHOULDN'T HAVE ENTERED THE RESERVATION --AND SLAUGHTERED THOSE ANIMALS!

AS THE GUARDIAN OF THE TRIBE, IT'S MY DUTY TO PUNISH THEM-- AND I WILL!

I CAN SENSE THEM JUST BEYOND THE NEXT RIDGE--!

THEY'RE CONFUSED! FRIGHTENED! THEY DON'T KNOW WHAT TO MAKE OF MY SCENT!

THEY'VE NEVER BEFORE FACED ANYTHING LIKE--

--PUMA!

WITH AN INCREDIBLE THIRTY-FIVE FOOT LEAP, THE MAN-BEAST KNOWN AS PUMA LAUNCHES HIMSELF FORWARD--!

HE ATTACKS SWIFTLY--

--WITH A STRENGTH WHICH STAGGERS THE MIND--

--AND A SAVAGERY FAR BEYOND THAT OF ANY WILD ANIMAL!

13

SIX MINUTES LATER...

THAT WASN'T A BAD MORNING'S WORKOUT! WITH LUCK, I CAN STILL CATCH THE TAIL END OF THE MEETING IN THE MAYOR'S OFFICE!

BLEEP! BLEEP!

SOUNDS LIKE JENNA'S BEEN TRYING TO CONTACT ME

SHE'S SO CAPABLE! I DON'T KNOW HOW I'D EVER SURVIVE WITHOUT HER!

BLEEP! BLEEP!

MOMENTS LATER...

PUMA SITS QUIETLY, DRAINING HIS MIND OF ALL TENSIONS...

HE SLOWS HIS BREATHING, AND BEGINS TO CONCENTRATE. CONCENTRATE!

AND THEN--

THE TRANSFORMATIONS SEEM TO BE GETTING EASIER...THOUGH THEY'RE JUST AS PAINFUL AS EVER!

I'D BETTER DISCUSS THEM WITH MY UNCLE AFTER THE NEXT MONTHLY TRIBAL MEETING!

I WISH I COULD CONVINCE THE OLD COOT TO MOVE OFF THE RESERVATION -- AND INTO A MODERN CONDOMINIUM IN HEARTSDALE -- BUT HE'S JUST TOO STUBBORN!

I'LL CHECK IN WITH THE OFFICE --

--AFTER I CHANGE INTO SOMETHING MORE CIVILIZED!

THERE! THAT'S BETTER!

I HOPE JENNA HAS EXCITING NEWS FOR ME! THINGS HAVE BEEN A BIT DULL AROUND HERE!

14

NEW YORK CITY...

WELL--? WHAT CAN I SAY, PETER?

THE QUALITY OF YOUR WORK IS CERTAINLY ON THE UPSWING--

J. ROBERTSON
EDITOR-IN-CHIEF

--EVEN IF YOUR CHOICE OF SUBJECT MATTER IS A LITTLE PEDESTRIAN!

OUR READERS HAVE SEEN COUNTLESS SHOTS OF SPIDER-MAN FIGHTING THUGS IN WAREHOUSES!

THE ONLY THING THAT MAKES THESE PARTICULAR PHOTOS NEWSWORTHY--

--IS THE FACT THAT THEY FEATURE THE WEB-SWINGER IN HIS NEW COSTUME!

I'LL TAKE THEM--

--BUT DON'T THINK YOU CAN COAST ON THE PUBLIC'S INTEREST IN THIS COSTUME FOREVER!

I -YAWN- WON'T!

TRY TO CONTROL YOUR ENTHUSIASM!

BETTY WILL PUT IN A VOUCHER FOR YOU.

DO YOURSELF A FAVOR--GET SOME REST!

YOU LOOK TERRIBLE!

ROBBY'S RIGHT! YOU DO SEEM A LITTLE ROUGH AROUND THE EDGES LATELY.

ARE THINGS ANY BETTER BETWEEN YOU AND YOUR AUNT?

NO.

AUNT MAY HAS REFUSED TO SPEAK TO ME EVER SINCE I TOLD HER THAT I'VE DROPPED OUT OF GRADUATE SCHOOL!*

* IN AMAZING SPIDER-MAN #253 -- DANNY.

15

I JUST DON'T KNOW WHAT TO DO, BETTY...

BRIGHTEN UP, TIGER!

IT'S PARTY TIME!

YOU--?

MARY JANE WATSON! IT'S ABOUT TIME YOU GOT HERE!

I WAS BEGINNING TO THINK THAT YOU HAD FORGOTTEN ALL ABOUT OUR DINNER DATE TONIGHT!

HI, PRETTY LADY! HOW'S IT ⸗YAWN⸗ GOING?

AM I BORING YOU ALREADY, MR. PARKER? MOST MEN I KNOW ARE USUALLY A LOT MORE EXCITED TO SEE ME.

DID BETTY TELL YOU THE BIG NEWS?

J. ROBERT
EDITOR-IN

I FOUND WORK! I LANDED A REGULAR MODELING GIG FOR THE NEXT FEW MONTHS! ISN'T THAT SIMPLY FABULOUS?!

I'M HAPPY FOR YOU!

BETTY AND I WERE PLANNING A LADIES' NIGHT OUT-- BUT THIS CALLS FOR A REAL CELEBRATION! CARE TO JOIN US?

GEE, I'D LOVE TO GO. I REALLY WOULD! BUT, I'VE GOT, ER, OTHER PLANS.

HOW ABOUT A RAINCHECK?

ANY TIME, TIGER!

GREAT! SEE YOU AROUND.

⸗WHEW⸗ TALK ABOUT A CLASSIC BRUSHOFF!

THERE GOES ONE VERY TROUBLED YOUNG MAN.

SO I NOTICED. ANY IDEA WHAT'S EATING AT HIM?

I HAVE A FEW THOUGHTS ON THE SUBJECT.

REALLY? I'D LIKE TO HEAR THEM...

16

AT THAT PRECISE MOMENT, A PRIVATE JET LANDS AT NEW YORK'S LAGUARDIA AIRPORT.

ITS SOLE OCCUPANT IS IMMEDIATELY USHERED INTO A WAITING LIMOUSINE.

SOON...

I APPRECIATE THE PROMPTNESS WITH WHICH YOU HAVE RESPONDED TO MY CALL.

THINK NOTHING OF IT. THE WORK YOU OFFER IS USUALLY SO... CHALLENGING.

I HAVE AN EXCEPTIONAL CHALLENGE FOR YOU THIS TIME.

HAVE YOU EVER HEARD OF A COSTUMED VIGILANTE WHO GOES BY THE NAME OF... "SPIDER-MAN"?

OF COURSE...

HE'S ONE OF THOSE SO-CALLED "SUPER-HEROES." THIS CITY CERTAINLY SEEMS TO HAVE AN ABUNDANCE OF THEM.

WE HAVE A FEW BASED IN MY PART OF THE COUNTRY AS WELL... THOUGH THEY AREN'T AS WELL-PUBLICIZED.

WILL YOU ACCEPT THIS CHALLENGE?

YES.

GOOD. WHEN SHALL YOU BEGIN?

IMMEDIATELY!

CAN YOU GET ME ANYTHING WHICH THIS SPIDER-MAN HAS RECENTLY HANDLED?

I ANTICIPATED YOUR NEED. I HAVE THIS PIECE OF PACKING CRATE. I MADE CERTAIN THAT NO ONE ELSE TOUCHED IT.

EXCELLENT.

MR. VARLEY WILL ESCORT YOU TO A PLACE WHERE YOU CAN CHANGE.

GOOD LUCK.

CALL ME IF YOU NEED ANYTHING!

THANK YOU.

I WON'T.

17

I'M GLAD I CAME.

THIS ASSIGNMENT HAS DEFINITE POSSIBILITIES!

CREEPY GUY.

YEAH.

WHAT DID THE ROSE SAY HIS NAME WAS--?

HE DIDN'T.

HE'S BEEN IN THERE FOR TWENTY MINUTES! HOW LONG DOES IT TAKE A GUY TO CHANGE HIS CLOTHES? WHAT'S HE DOING?

BEATS ME.

HELLO--? IS EVERYTHING ALL RIGHT?

NOK! NOK!

I DON'T LIKE THIS! NOT ONE BIT!

WHY AIN'T HE ANSWERING?

VARLEY, SOMETHING TELLS ME WE BETTER OPEN THAT DOOR...

HEY! HE'S GONE--!

I DON'T GET IT! HE LEFT HIS CLOTHES BEHIND!

LOOK! THE WINDOW--!

HE COULDN'T HAVE GOTTEN OUT THIS WAY! THE NEAREST ROOFTOP HAS GOTTA BE A GOOD FORTY FEET AWAY!

18

NEARBY... AH! THE LIFE OF A MILLIONAIRE ENTREPRENEUR MAY HAVE ITS DISTINCT PLEASURES, BUT THEY CAN'T COMPARE WITH THIS--!

OF COURSE, MY UNCLE WOULD HAVE A FIT--IF HE EVER LEARNED THAT HIS BELOVED TRIBAL GUARDIAN WAS ALSO AN ASSASSIN FOR HIRE!

THAT'S HIS PROBLEM!

HE'S GOT NOTHING TO COMPLAIN ABOUT AS LONG AS I CONTINUE TO FULFILL MY OBLIGATIONS TO THE TRIBE!

THE WAY I CHOOSE TO ENTERTAIN MYSELF IS NOBODY'S BUSINESS BUT MY OWN!

I JUST HOPE SPIDER-MAN LIVES UP TO HIS REP! IT'S BEEN FAR TOO LONG SINCE I BATTLED ANYONE WORTH THE EFFORT.

HHM! THE SPOOR IS WEAK...BUT I THINK I'VE IDENTIFIED HIS SCENT!

NOW, COMES THE HARD PART....

I MUST BLOCK OUT ALL PHYSICAL AND MENTAL DISTRACTIONS!

MUST CHANNEL EVERYTHING...ALL CONSCIOUSNESS ...THE VERY ESSENCE OF MY BEING...

...INTO A SINGLE, HEIGHTENED SENSE!

IT IS SAID THAT EVERY LIVING THING HAS ITS OWN, UNIQUE SCENT...

IN A CITY WHOSE POPULATION NUMBERS IN THE MILLIONS, PUMA ATTEMPTS TO PINPOINT ONE MAN...

ONE VERY SPECIAL MAN...

FOR MORE THAN AN HOUR HE SITS RIGID AS STONE...

SORTING...

SEARCHING...

AND THEN...

I'VE DONE IT! I'VE FOUND HIM!

INCREDIBLY POWERFUL LEG MUSCLES PROPEL HIM UPWARD AND FORWARD ON A DIRECT ROUTE TO HIS PREY!

19

MEANWHILE...

≷YAWN≷ WHY DO I ALWAYS SEEM TO HAVE SO MUCH TROUBLE MANAGING MY OWN LIFE?

I JUST CAN'T THINK OF A WAY TO PATCH THINGS UP BETWEEN ME AND AUNT MAY!

THE WOMAN PRACTICALLY RAISED ME! SHE'S ALWAYS BEEN ONE OF THE CORNER-STONES OF MY LIFE!

≷YAWN≷ THERE'S GOTTA BE A SOLU-TION! MAYBE I'M JUST TOO ZONKED TO SEE IT!

SO THAT'S SPIDER-MAN--!

HOW DISAPPOINTING! I'D HOPED FOR SOMEONE MUCH MORE IMPRESSIVE! BIGGER! MORE POWERFUL!

THERE MUST BE MORE TO HIM THAN MEETS THE EYE!

PERHAPS A LITTLE TEST IS IN ORDER--!

RIPP!

AND, AS IF I DIDN'T HAVE ENOUGH PROBLEMS, THERE'S THE LITTLE MATTER OF THE HOBGOBLIN'S MISSING BATTLE VAN!

IT VANISHED ON ITS WAY TO THE POLICE IMPOUND YARD!*

WHO TOOK IT...AND, MORE IMPORTANTLY, WHY--?

HEY! MY SPIDER-SENSE--!

WHAT THE--?!

*IN ISSUE #254--DANNY.

20

YEOW!

WHATEVER THAT THING WAS -- I BARELY DUCKED IT!

I WAS SO TOTALLY LOST IN MY THOUGHTS THAT I DIDN'T EVEN NOTICE MY SPIDER-SENSE BUZZING!

CAN'T WORRY ABOUT THAT NOW!

GOTTA TRY TO SLOW MY FALL--!

DESPERATE, ACTING ON INSTINCT ALONE, SPIDER-MAN REACHES OUT TOWARD THE NEARBY BUILDING...

HIS FINGERS SCRAPE ALONG ITS ROUGH EDGE --

-- UNTIL HE MANAGES TO FLATTEN THEM AGAINST THE SIDE OF THE BUILDING!

AND THEN, OWING TO HIS UNCANNY ABILITY TO ADHERE TO ANY SURFACE --

-- THEY HOLD!

ARGGG!

MY ARM--!

SNAP!

FWOK!

F-FEELS LIKE I WRENCHED IT LOOSE FROM ITS SOCKET--!

PAIN IS INCREDIBLE!

G-GOTTA GET MYSELF TOGETHER--!

WHOEVER ATTACKED ME IS STILL OUT THERE! WAITING--!

UHHH!

21

NEXT ISSUE! THE BLACK CAT ENRAGED! A STARTLING REVELATION FROM MARY JANE WATSON--WHICH WILL CHANGE PETER PARKER'S LIFE FOREVER! PLUS--THE SURPRISING RETURN OF THE MOST REQUESTED SPIDER-VILLAIN OF RECENT TIMES! (GUESS WHO!) DON'T MISS--

"THE FURY OF... PUMA!"

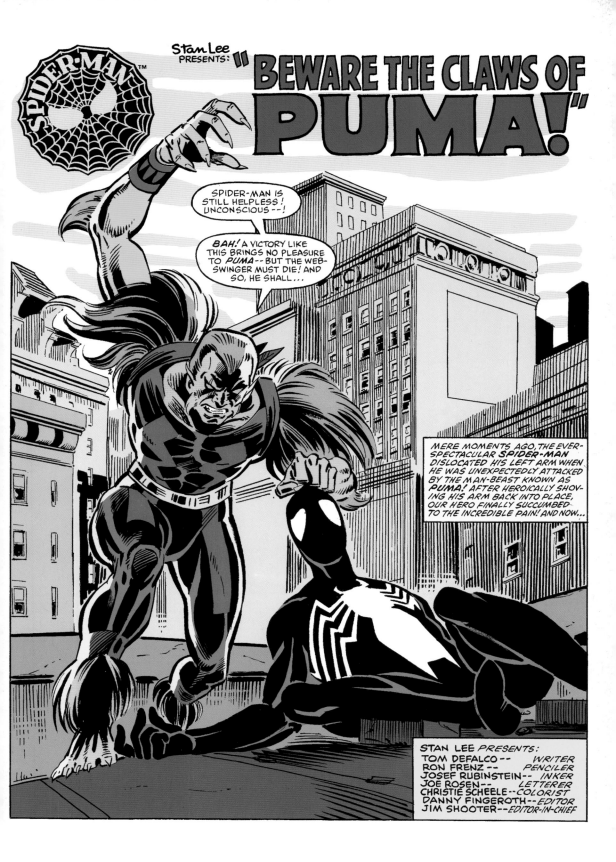

THIS IS ALMOST TOO EASY!

WHEN THE *ROSE* FIRST HIRED ME TO KILL SPIDER-MAN, HE PROMISED ME A WORTHY FOE!

A TRUE CHALLENGE TO THE POWER OF *PUMA*!

THE ROSE LIED!

SPIDER-MAN IS A WEAKLING! A COWARD!

HE DESERVES TO DIE!

NO!

CVJAM!

⇟UGNN⇞

MANAGED TO RECOVER MY BALANCE, BUT SHE'S ATTACKING AGAIN--!

⇟WHOOPS⇞ MISSED 'IM!

YOU'RE GOOD, MISTER! *FAST!* AGILE, TOO!

DO NOT FLATTER YOURSELF, WOMAN!

A CHILD COULD HAVE DODGED THAT CLUMSY ATTACK!

THIS WOMAN IS THE *BLACK CAT!* THE NEWSPAPERS CLAIM THERE IS A ROMANTIC LINK BETWEEN HER AND SPIDER-MAN. A PITY THAT SHE ISN'T A PART OF MY CONTRACT WITH THE ROSE!

GO AWAY, WOMAN! THIS ISN'T YOUR CONCERN! DON'T FORCE ME TO KILL YOU AS WELL!

2

GET REAL, MISTER! I DON'T KNOW WHO YOU ARE, OR WHAT YOU WANT--

--BUT YOU'RE DEFINITELY FLAKE CITY IF YOU THINK I'LL LET YOU HURT MY SPIDER!

YOU CAN'T STOP ME!

I AM PUMA!

WAIT--! THERE SEEMS TO BE SOMETHING SURROUNDING THAT WOMAN! AN AURA OF SOME KIND!

I'M SURE MY HEIGHTENED SENSES WILL BE ABLE TO DETECT IT--IF I CAN JUST FOCUS THEM PROPERLY...

"THERE! I SEE IT NOW!"

I WONDER IF IT'S DANGEROUS?

GUESS THERE'S ONLY ONE WAY TO FIND OUT!

POWERFUL LEG MUSCLES PROPEL HIM FORWARD--

--BUT THEN...

WHAT'S WRONG WITH ME? I SEEM TO HAVE MISJUDGED THE DISTANCE BETWEEN US!

I'M OVERSHOOTING HER--!

GOING TOO FAST! HAVE TO SLOW MYSELF DOWN BEFORE I GO BOUNDING OFF THE SIDE OF THIS ROOF!

THAT PIPE--!

SNAPP!

OH, NO!

FWOK!

3

NOTHING LIKE THAT HAS EVER HAPPENED TO ME BEFORE! MY SENSE OF BALANCE IS PERFECT!

COULD THE CAT'S MYSTERIOUS AURA HAVE CAUSED IT?

SEEKING TO CONFIRM HIS SUSPICIONS, PUMA SPRINGS TO HIS FEET, RENEWING HIS ONSLAUGHT ON THE CAT...

BUT THEN...

THE ROOF--! IT'S GIVING WAY BENEATH ME!

KRACKKK!

TA-TA, FUR FACE!

NOW YOU KNOW WHAT HAPPENS WHEN THE BLACK CAT CROSSES YOUR PATH!

÷UNNN÷

SPIDER! YOU'RE AWAKE--!

C-CAT, IS THAT YOU?

WHO ELSE?

DON'T WORRY ABOUT THAT CLOWN WHO ATTACKED YOU, HON! I JUST TOOK CARE OF HIM!

HEY! YOU DON'T LOOK SO GOOD! ANYTHING I CAN DO TO HELP--?

AGGH! MY SHOULDER--!

OH, I'M SO SORRY! I...I DIDN'T KNOW!

H-HOW COULD YOU? I... INJURED IT IN A FREAK FALL! IT STILL HURTS, BUT NOT AS BAD AS IT DID EARLIER!

THIS WEBBING SHOULD HELP KEEP THE STRAIN OFF IT!

LOOK, WE'D BETTER GET OUT OF HERE!

PWIP!

ARE YOU SURE YOU CAN TRAVEL?

NO, BUT I CAN TRY!

MINUTES LATER...

POOR SPIDER! HE'S PUTTING UP A BRAVE FRONT FOR MY SAKE, BUT IT'S OBVIOUS THAT HE'S IN GREAT PAIN!

HANG ON, LOVER! YOUR APARTMENT IS ONLY A FEW BLOCKS AWAY!

4

MEANWHILE...

HEY! WHAT'S GOING ON?

WHO ARE YOU?

BE SILENT--! I HAVE NEITHER THE TIME, NOR THE INCLINATION TO ANSWER YOUR STUPID QUESTIONS!

GET OUT OF MY WAY, WOMAN!

OH--!

H-HE'S LEAVING, BILL! BUT WHAT ABOUT OUR CEILING--?

H-HUSH UP, ALICE! LET THE MAN GO ABOUT HIS BUSINESS!

MOMENTS LATER, ON THE BUILDING'S ROOFTOP...

SPIDER-MAN AND THE BLACK CAT ARE GONE--!

THE FOOLS! THEY CAN'T ESCAPE PUMA!

NO ONE CAN!

NOW THAT I'VE BEEN EXPOSED TO THEIR INDIVIDUAL SCENTS --

-- I CAN EASILY TRACK THEM TO WHEREVER THEY HIDE!

I'D BETTER APPROACH THE BLACK CAT WITH A BIT MORE CAUTION, THOUGH! SHE'S OBVIOUSLY THE MORE DANGEROUS OF THE TWO!

HER AURA SEEMED TO FLASH BRIGHTER BOTH TIMES I ATTACKED HER!

COINCIDENCE? I THINK NOT! THAT AURA MUST BE RESPONSIBLE FOR THE MISFORTUNE WHICH STRUCK ME!

LOST IN HIS THOUGHTS, PUMA BOUNDS FROM BUILDING TO BUILDING IN PURSUIT OF HIS PREY, UNTIL ...

THERE THEY ARE! ON THAT DISTANT ROOFTOP--!

5

HOLD IT, CAT! MY SPIDER-SENSE IS TINGLING!

I SENSE DANGER--!

WHAT COULD IT BE--?

I DON'T SEE ANYTHING OUT OF THE ORDINARY! MAYBE I'M JUST JUMPY.

HE'S FAST--! I BARELY GOT DOWN IN TIME!

NO NEED TO CONTINUE THIS BATTLE NOW! I'M ONLY BEING PAID TO KILL SPIDER-MAN. WHY SHOULD I KILL THE CAT FOR FREE?

I'LL RETURN LATER ...AFTER I'VE HAD A CHANCE TO REFRESH MYSELF!

MEANWHILE... EASY DOES IT, LOVER. YOU'RE HOME NOW.

YEAH...

THANKS, CAT. I MIGHT NOT HAVE MADE IT WITHOUT YOU.

MY ARM'S STILL THROBBING.

BUT AT LEAST I WON'T HAVE TO WRESTLE WITH MY COSTUME TO GET A LOOK AT IT! ALL I HAVE TO DO IS--

UNNN SPIDER--! WHAT IS IT?

MY COSTUME--!

IT USUALLY OBEYS MY EVERY THOUGHT, BUT IT'S NOT RESPONDING TO MY MENTAL COMMANDS--!

I CAN'T SEEM TO GET IT TO LEAVE ME--!

UGNNN AT LAST! IT'S STARTING TO MELT OFF ME...

I DON'T UNDERSTAND ...IT NEVER GAVE ME A PROBLEM BEFORE! WHAT COULD BE WRONG WITH IT?

ARE YOU KIDDING!? LOOK AT IT SNAKING ACROSS THE FLOOR LIKE THAT--!

WHAT COULD BE RIGHT WITH IT?

YOU'VE BEEN MEANING TO GET IT CHECKED OUT BY REED RICHARDS EVER SINCE YOU BROUGHT IT BACK FROM THAT WAR AT THE OTHER END OF THE UNIVERSE!

I KNOW. BUT MY LIFE HAS BEEN SO CRAZY LATELY THAT I HAVEN'T HAD TIME.

MAYBE YOU'D BETTER MAKE TIME.

*SEE THE ONGOING MARVEL SUPER HEROES SECRET WARS LIMITED SERIES FOR DETAILS --DANNY.

HEY! MY ARM DOESN'T LOOK A' BAD AS I FE' ED--!

IT'LL PROBABLY BE AWFUL SORE FOR THE NEXT FEW WEEKS, BUT THERE DOESN'T SEEM TO BE ANY PERMANENT DAMAGE!

THAT'S GREAT!

WHAT A DUMP! I STILL CAN'T BELIEVE MY SPIDER REALLY LIVES HERE IN HIS CIVILIAN IDENTITY!

GUESS I JUST DON'T UNDERSTAND SPIDER. WHY WOULD HE EVER WANT TO BE A NORMAL PERSON LIKE PETER PARKER, WHEN HE COULD BE SPIDER-MAN ALL THE TIME?

I LOVE HIM. I DO! BUT NOW THAT HE'S TAKEN OFF HIS MASK, I CAN HARDLY BEAR TO LOOK AT HIM...

MEANWHILE, AT A MIDTOWN MANHATTAN SKYSCRAPER...

AS PER YOUR INSTRUCTIONS...

...I HAVE BEGUN MAKING THE NECESSARY ARRANGEMENTS FOR A PROLONGED GANG WAR WITH THE FORCES OF MICAH SYNN!*

EXCELLENT. I LEAVE THE DETAILS TO YOU!

*SEE CURRENT ISSUES OF DAREDEVIL -- DANNY.

ONE LAST ITEM-- AS THE KINGPIN OF CRIME, THE RULER OF THE UNDERWORLD, YOU MUST BE MADE AWARE OF THE FACT THAT SOMEONE IN YOUR EMPLOY HAS HIRED A PROFESSIONAL ASSASSIN TO ELIMINATE SPIDER-MAN!

WHAT--?!

I HAVE MY OWN PLANS FOR THE WEB-SWINGER!*

WHO WOULD DARE ORDER AN EXECUTION OF THIS MAGNITUDE-- WITHOUT FIRST CONSULTING WITH ME?

I BELIEVE THIS HIT WAS COMMISSIONED BY THE ROSE!

*AND YOU'LL KNOW WHAT PLANS THE KINGPIN IS REFERRING TO, IF YOU KEEP READING OUR COMPANION MAGAZINE, THE SPECTACULAR SPIDER-MAN--D.

ARRANGE A MEETING BETWEEN ME AND THE ROSE. IT'S TIME HE LEARNED THE FACTS OF LIFE...

...AND DEATH!

7

A FEW BLOCKS AWAY, AT THE *SAINT LAUREN SUMMIT*, ONE OF THE CITY'S MORE PRESTIGIOUS HOTELS...

...IN THE LUXURY SUITE RESERVED FOR *THOMAS FIREHEART*...

AH! NOTHING REFRESHES LIKE A HOT SHOWER!

I KNOW IT'S LATE, BUT I REALLY SHOULD CHECK IN WITH MY HOME OFFICE!

HEARTSDALE, NEW MEXICO...

FIREHEART ENTERPRISES...

THOMAS! I'M GLAD YOU CALLED.

GOOD NEWS. CONGRESSMAN CRESPI PHONED EARLIER TO SAY THAT THE CITY COUNCIL AP-PROVED--

"--THREE OF THE FOUR SITES FOR THE NEW SHOPPING MALLS YOU PLANNED TO BUILD!"

EXCELLENT!

I DON'T KNOW WHAT I'D DO WITHOUT JENNA TAYLOR TO RUN THINGS WHILE I WAS AWAY!

JUST HAVE TO MAKE ONE MORE CALL--

"--TO THE *ROSE!*"

IT'S FOR YOU, BOSS. THE PUMA!

GOOD EVENING, MY FRIEND...I TRUST ALL IS GOING WELL. YOU EXPECT TO COMPLETE YOUR MISSION TONIGHT? EXCELLENT!

B-ZIT

WHO CAN THAT BE?

I AM THE ARRANGER, AND I BRING YOU GREETINGS FROM--

--THE KINGPIN OF CRIME!

8

THE ROSE SEEMED A BIT DISTRACTED WHEN HE HUNG UP. I HOPE NOTHING'S WRONG. I HAVE YET TO COLLECT MY FEE.

HHM! I'M GLAD I REMEMBERED TO BRING A SPARE COSTUME, THE ONE I WORE EARLIER IS STILL IN DESPERATE NEED OF A GOOD DRY CLEANING.

A PITY I COULDN'T TRUST IT TO THE HOTEL'S VALET SERVICE--

--BUT THAT'S NOT AN OPTION IF ONE WISHES TO KEEP HIS IDENTITY A SECRET!

I MUST NOW DRIVE AWAY ALL EXTERNAL DISTRACTIONS...

MUST MARSHAL ALL OF MY THOUGHTS AND FOCUS INWARD...

MUST CONCENTRATE...

CONCENTRATE...

≥ARGGH≤

MOMENTS LATER, COVERING AN UNBELIEVABLE THIRTY-FIVE FEET WITH EVERY LEAP, THE PUMA BOUNDS ACROSS THE CITY'S ROOFTOPS...

THE HUNT IS ON!

AND, AT 410 CHELSEA STREET...

FEELING ANY BETTER--?

9

A LITTLE! TELL ME MORE ABOUT THAT JOKER WHO ATTACKED ME!

THERE REALLY ISN'T MUCH MORE... EXCEPT TO SAY THAT HE WAS VERY KINKY-LOOKING! ALL COVERED WITH FUR!

CALLED HIMSELF... "PUMA"!

LIKE THE RUNNING SHOE--?! ≈SHEESH≈ WHERE DO THEY COME UP WITH THESE HOKEY NAMES?

WHO KNOWS? I WOULDN'T WORRY ABOUT HIM, THOUGH. CONSIDERING THE WAY I CLOBBERED HIM THIS AFTERNOON, HE'D BE A FOOL TO RETURN FOR A REMATCH!

Y'KNOW, YOU NEVER DID TELL ME EXACTLY HOW YOU MANAGED TO BEAT HIM...

UH-OH! THIS ISN'T THE TIME TO TELL SPIDER ABOUT MY BAD LUCK POWERS! WE'LL DISCUSS THAT LATER! RIGHT NOW, I'VE GOT TO BOOGIE--!

YOU'RE LEAVING? NOW--?!

WHY NOT? YOU CERTAINLY DON'T NEED ME TO NURSEMAID YOU ANYMORE! BESIDES, YOU KNOW HOW I HATE TO BE COOPED UP AT NIGHT!

WHAT ABOUT THIS PUMA CHARACTER? YOU MIGHT RUN INTO HIM AGAIN--!

SO? I'LL GIVE HIM YOUR REGARDS!

DON'T WORRY ABOUT ME, LOVER! I'LL BE BACK BEFORE YOU KNOW IT!

I'M JUST GONNA CATCH SOME FRESH AIR!

IT'S A SHAME I HAVE TO DESERT SPIDER LIKE THIS--

--BUT I WAS GOING STIR CRAZY IN THAT DREARY APART-MENT!

WHAT A HOLE! I'VE BEEN IN MAUSOLEUMS WHICH WERE LIVELIER!

SPRINGING TO A NEARBY BUILDING, THE BLACK CAT RACES INTO THE DEEPENING NIGHT...

10

AT LAST!

SPIDER-MAN IS ALONE! UNPROTECTED--!

AT THAT MOMENT...

PETER! YOU HOME--?

KNOK KNOK

THAT VOICE! CAN IT REALLY BE HER--?!

MARY JANE WATSON!

SURPRISED, TIGER? GOOD! I LIKE TO KEEP MY MEN OFF BALANCE!

YOU LOOKED A LITTLE DOWN THE LAST TIME I SAW YOU*...SO I DROPPED BY TO BUOY YOUR SPIRITS! HERE--! I EVEN BROUGHT MY OWN WINE!

* SEE LAST ISSUE-- DANNY.

HEY! WHAT'S WITH THE DAMAGED WING? WHAT HAPPENED?!

IT'S NOTHING! I, ER, SPRAINED IT PLAYING RACQUETBALL.

GLAD TO HEAR IT ISN'T SERIOUS! I'D HATE FOR ANYTHING TO SPOIL OUR LITTLE PARTY!

WE HAVE SOME HEAVY CELEBRATING TO DO! I FINALLY MANAGED TO FIND STEADY MODELING WORK, AND I'M WALKING ON AIR!

THAT'S GREAT, MJ! I--

UH-OH! MY SPIDER-SENSE JUST KICKED IN! THERE'S DANGER--

11

INCREDIBLE! THAT...THAT THING... LEAPED ACROSS THE ROOM AND MOLDED ITSELF AROUND SPIDER-MAN'S BODY! IF I HADN'T WITNESSED IT WITH MY OWN EYES--!

PUMA SHALL MAKE YOUR DEATH AS SWIFT--AND PAINLESS--AS POSSIBLE!

GEE, THAT'S AWFULLY SPORTING OF YOU!

SO YOU'RE PUMA! NOW THAT WE'VE MET, I'D LIKE TO FORMALLY INTRODUCE YOU TO MY KNUCKLES!

≥UNH!≤ SHOULDN'T HAVE PULLED MY PUNCH! HIS JAW IS A LOT HARDER THAN IT LOOKS!

FWOK!

ARGGH!

SKRITCH!

FOOL! IT WILL TAKE MUCH MORE THAN A SINGLE BLOW TO STOP PUMA!

YOUR COSTUME--! CAN THE EVIDENCE OF MY HEIGHTENED SENSES BE TRUE?

NO! IT...IT JUST ISN'T POSSIBLE!

DOES MY COSTUME SPOOK YOU? IT SHOULD! IT CAME FROM AN ALIEN WORLD IN A DISTANT GALAXY--

--AND IT'S CAPABLE OF SOME PRETTY AMAZING TRICKS!

≥UNNN≤ I WISH MY BACK COULD HEAL ITSELF JUST AS QUICKLY!

MEANWHILE, OUTSIDE...

CAN'T HEAR WHAT'S BEING SAID BEHIND THIS DOOR, BUT ALL THAT CRASHING AROUND MEANS PETER'S IN TROUBLE! BIG TROUBLE!

PETER! PETER! ARE YOU ALL RIGHT IN THERE?

BWAM!

PETER--!

LET ME IN! PLEASE--!

13

BWAK!

FWAM!

IT'S NO USE! PUMA HAS THE ADVANTAGE IN CLOSE QUARTERS! I'VE GOT TO LURE HIM OUTSIDE-- WHERE I'LL HAVE MORE ROOM TO MANEUVER!

WHY DO YOU SEEK TO PROLONG THE INEVITABLE? YOU CAN'T AVOID ME FOREVER!

NO, BUT I CAN HAVE A LOT OF FUN TRYING--!

HE'S IN THE RIGHT SPOT AT LAST!

BANZAI!

THERE! HE DIDN'T EXPECT ME TO SUDDENLY SPRING FORWARD!

KRA--ASH!

NOW, IF ONLY I CAN DIRECT OUR FALL--!

AND, AT THAT PRECISE MOMENT...

I DID IT! I FINALLY MANAGED TO FORCE THE DOOR OPEN!

FWOOK!

I'M HERE, PETER! I'M...

PETER--! HE...HE'S GONE!

14

JUST THEN, AT A CERTAIN MIDTOWN SKYSCRAPER...

PLEASE MAKE YOURSELF COMFORTABLE...

...AS COMFORTABLE AS POSSIBLE!

WE HAVE MUCH TO DISCUSS!

ROSE, IT HAS COME TO MY NOTICE THAT YOU TOOK IT UPON YOURSELF TO ORDER THE EXECUTION OF SPIDER-MAN WITHOUT FIRST CONSULTING WITH ME!

EXPLAIN YOURSELF!

THE WEB-SWINGER WAS DISRUPTING MY OPERATIONS, MAKING IT DIFFICULT FOR ME TO RAISE MY MONTHLY REVENUE QUOTAS. SO, I ATTEMPTED TO SOLVE THE PROBLEM.

I FIND YOUR SOLUTION UN-ACCEPTABLE!

I DO NOT CHOOSE TO HAVE SPIDER-MAN KILLED...AT THIS TIME!

I TRUST MY POSITION IS CLEAR!

YES.

QUITE CLEAR.

ELSEWHERE...

PUMA! THIS IS CRAZY! INSANE--! WE'VE NEVER EVEN MET BEFORE TODAY! WHY ARE WE FIGHTING?

THE REASONS SHOULD BE OBVIOUS! YOU WISH TO PROLONG YOUR LIFE--

-- WHILE I AM DETERMINED TO END IT!

15

17

-- AND, IN THIS CASE, IT'S *ME!*

PWIP!

PWIP!

SPWOT

AMAZING--!

HE MANAGED TO WEB MY WEAPON TO THE WALL... JUST AS I WAS ABOUT TO THROW IT!

‡UGN‡ CAN'T RIP IT FREE!

WAIT--! CAN MY HEIGHTENED SENSES BE TELLING ME THE TRUTH?!

I HAD ALWAYS ASSUMED THAT SPIDER-MAN'S WEBBING WAS SOMETHING ARTIFICIAL-- A MAN-MADE SUBSTANCE-- BUT NOW, AFTER TOUCHING IT, I REALIZE I WAS WRONG!

IT'S ORGANIC!

"ORGANIC"?!

ARE YOU SURE--?!

STOP TRYING TO PLAY ME FOR A FOOL, SPIDER-MAN! THAT ONLY SERVES TO INCREASE MY FURY--!

YOU MUST KNOW WHAT YOUR WEBBING'S COMPOSED OF--!

YEOW!

CAN'T ARGUE WITH PUMA NOW!

THAT'S A TON AND A HALF OF UNIVERSAL GYM BEARING DOWN ON ME! GOT TO LEAP ASIDE--!

18

BUT THEN, EVEN AS SPIDER-MAN BOUNDS TO SAFETY--

SPWAMM!

NO--! I SHOULDN'T HAVE LOST MY TEMPER LIKE THAT! INNOCENT LIVES WILL BE LOST WHEN THAT THING HITS THE STREET!

PWIP!

SPIDER-MAN! STOP--! WHERE DO YOU THINK YOU'RE--

"--GOING?!"

IT'S A GOOD THING I CAN STICK TO ANY SURFACE, BECAUSE I'VE GOTTA ANCHOR MYSELF TO THIS WALL--

--AND PRAY THAT THERE'S STILL TIME TO PREVENT THAT ONE TON TERROR FROM SQUASHING ANYONE!

TRIGGERED BY SPIDER-MAN'S THOUGHTS, TWIN STRANDS OF WEBBING RACE TOWARD THE PLUMMETING UNIVERSAL--

--SNAGGING IT IN MID-AIR--!

THOUGH THE WEBBING IS STRETCHED TO ITS MAXIMUM CAPABILITIES, IT HOLDS!

BUT...

ARGH--PAIN IN MY ARM--! UNBELIEVABLE! BUT I GOTTA HOLD ON--!

RIPPP!

OH, NO! THE WALL CAN'T CAN'T SUPPORT THE ADDED WEIGHT! I'M BEING PULLED FREE--!

19

QUAMM!

IF SPIDER-MAN HADN'T DIVERTED THAT THING--!

WHAT ABOUT THE WEB-SWINGER HIMSELF?

"--HE'S FALLING!"

MUST REMAIN CALM! LIMP--!

IF I CAN HIT THE ROOF OF THAT BUS JUST RIGHT, THE IMPACT WILL BE EQUALLY DISTRIBUTED ACROSS MY ENTIRE BODY! IF NOT--

KA-VWAM!

SPIDER-MAN APPEARS TO HAVE SURVIVED HIS FALL! *GOOD!* HE IS A COURAGEOUS FOE--AND DESERVES A BETTER DEATH!

I COULD EASILY CRUSH HIM NOW...

...BUT THAT WOULD BE UNWORTHY OF ME!

I PREFER TO WAIT UNTIL HE HAS HAD A CHANCE TO RECOVER--TO REGAIN HIS FULL POWER!

ONLY THEN, WILL PUMA RETURN--

--TO CLAIM A VICTORY WORTH SAVORING!

PUMA'S GETTING AWAY! SWELL--! I'M NOT IN ANY SHAPE TO GO CHASING AFTER HIM! WONDER WHEN WE'LL MEET AGAIN?

SOMETIME LATER, AT THE *SAINT LAUREN SUMMIT...*

ONCE I FINISH PACKING, I'LL PHONE THE ROSE AND INFORM HIM OF MY DECISION TO TEMPORARILY POSTPONE OUR CONTRACT!

BING BONG

THE DOORBELL!

HIYA, PAL. WE'VE GOT A MESSAGE FOR YOU... FROM THE ROSE.

REALLY?

PLEASE COME IN...

20

HOW DID PUMA RE-ACT TO THE NEWS THAT WE WERE CANCELING HIS CONTRACT?

REAL GOOD. IN FACT, HE LOOKED A LITTLE RELIEVED...

I TRUST YOU INFORMED HIM THAT HE WILL BE ADEQUATELY COMPENSATED FOR HIS TIME--?

YEAH! HE WAS PLEASED TO HEAR THAT, TOO!

WHAT ABOUT THE KINGPIN, BOSS? ARE YOU GOING TO LET HIM GET AWAY WITH MUSCLING YOU AROUND?

ONE MUST BE A REALIST IN THESE MATTERS, MR. JOHNSTON. THE KINGPIN OF CRIME CURRENT-LY HOLDS ALL THE CARDS. IT WOULD BE PURE SUICIDE TO DEFY HIM.

PERHAPS THAT CAN CHANGE...WITH *MY* HELP!

WHO--?!

ALLOW ME TO INTRODUCE MYSELF! I AM...

HOBGOBLIN!

FOR A SEEMINGLY ETERNAL INSTANT, THE ROSE STUDIES THE MYSTERIOUS FIGURE WHO HOVERS IN THE AIR BEFORE HIM!

AND THEN, BENEATH HIS LEATHER MASK, THE ROSE BEGINS TO SMILE! *AND PLAN--!*

21

AT THAT EXACT MOMENT, A TAXI DISCHARGES A PASSENGER AT 410 CHELSEA STREET...

HOME AT LAST! THAT TUSSLE WITH PUMA LEFT ME SO WRECKED-- THAT I BARELY HAD ENOUGH STRENGTH TO CHANGE INTO MY CIVVIES-- AND FLAG DOWN THIS HACK!

÷ WHEW ÷ WHAT A DAY! MY BACK IS KILLING ME, AND MY ARM FEELS WORSE!

AND MY MIND IS BUZZING WITH SO MANY UNANSWERED QUESTIONS!

WHY DID PUMA ATTACK ME IN THE FIRST PLACE? WHY DIDN'T HE FINISH ME OFF WHEN HE HAD THE CHANCE?

HHM! SOUNDS LIKE SOMEONE'S INSIDE MY APARTMENT! I WONDER IF FELICIA'S BACK--?

MARY JANE--?!

OMIGOSH, I HAD FORGOTTEN ALL ABOUT HER!

PETER--! YOU'RE BACK! YOU'RE SAFE--!

ALL THAT CRASHING AND SHOUTING--! I THOUGHT I'D GO OUT OF MY MIND!

EVERYTHING'S ALL RIGHT, MJ! THOSE SOUNDS YOU HEARD WERE ONLY, ER, ONLY...

YOU DON'T HAVE TO MAKE UP ANOTHER ONE OF YOUR PHONY EXCUSES, PETER! NOT NOW--!

I KNOW THE TRUTH! THE REAL TRUTH!

WHAT ARE YOU TALKING ABOUT?

I'VE KNOWN YOUR SECRET FOR YEARS! UP UNTIL TODAY, I ALWAYS THOUGHT I COULD COPE WITH IT IF I EVER HAD TO EXPERIENCE IT FIRSTHAND-- BUT I CAN'T! I CAN'T--!

I JUST CAN'T COPE WITH THE FACT THAT PETER PARKER IS SECRETLY SPIDER-MAN!

TO BE CONTINUED--!

MY SECRET IDENTITY--! SHE KNOWS!

SHE KNOWS!

THIS IS ALL PUMA'S FAULT! IF ONLY HIS SUPER-SENSES HADN'T LED HIM HERE WHILE MARY JANE WAS VISITING--!*

MY SPIDER-SENSE WARNED ME OF HIS APPROACH IN SUFFICIENT TIME TO SHOVE HER INTO THE HALLWAY-- OUT OF HARM'S WAY-- BUT SHE MUST HAVE HEARD THE COMMOTION WHEN HE ATTACKED ME!

*SEE LAST ISSUE FOR DETAILS-- DANNY.

MARY JANE! WAIT--!

WE HAVE TO TALK!

WHAT'S THE USE, PETER?

YOU'RE ONLY GOING TO LIE TO ME!

YOU'LL DENY EVERYTHING, AND I REALLY CAN'T BLAME YOU!

AFTER ALL, HOW COULD YOU EVER CONFIDE IN AN AIRHEAD LIKE MARY JANE WATSON?!?

MARY JANE, PLEASE--!

I CARE ABOUT YOU, PETER! I REALLY DO! BUT YOU COME WITH SO MUCH BAGGAGE! YOU CAN'T IMAGINE HOW HARD IT IS TO ACCEPT THE FACT THAT ONE OF MY CLOSEST FRIENDS IS CONSTANTLY OUT RISKING HIS LIFE!

THAT'S WHY I ORIGINALLY LEFT NEW YORK!

I JUST COULDN'T TAKE IT ANYMORE!

I HAD TO GET AWAY FROM YOU... AND SPIDER-MAN!

UH-OH! AS IF I DIDN'T HAVE ENOUGH TO WORRY ABOUT, I SENSE SOMEONE OUTSIDE MY WINDOW--!

HAS PUMA RETURNED TO STRIKE AGAIN?!

2

OH--!

WHAT'S HAPPENING, LOVER? I JUST STOPPED BY TO--

÷WHOOPS÷

IT'S TRUE. IT'S ALL TRUE!

OH, *NO!* THE BLACK CAT JUST BLEW MY SECRET IDENTITY FOR SURE!

I...I GUESS I SHOULD BE GOING!

NO!

OF COURSE SHE SHOULD GO! SHE DOESN'T BELONG HERE!

MARY JANE, DON'T--!

CAT, PLEASE--!

WHO IS SHE?

WHAT'S SHE DOING HERE?

WHY DON'T YOU ANSWER ME?

GOODBYE, PETER!

MARY JANE!

PLEASE

DON'T

GO

PLEASE...

LET HER GO, LOVER! YOU DON'T NEED THAT BIMBO!

WHO *IS* SHE ANYWAY?

3

SHE'S A FRIEND, CAT! *A FRIEND!* BUT YOU JUST RUINED EVERYTHING!

HOW MANY TIMES HAVE I WARNED YOU ABOUT COMING IN MY FRONT WINDOW? *HOW MANY?!*

NO SALE, PARTNER! I'M NOT TAKING ANY OF YOUR GRIEF! NOT NOW--!

YOU'RE JUST MAD 'CAUSE I SCARED YOUR CUTIE!

WELL, I'M GLAD I DID! I THOUGHT WE HAD AN UNDERSTANDING! I THOUGHT YOU LOVED ME--!

I GUESS I WAS WRONG...

NO, CAT! *WAIT--!* YOU DON'T UNDERSTAND!

NO! I WON'T LET YOU RUN OUT ON ME, TOO!

PWIP!

SUDDENLY, A SLENDER STRAND OF WEBBING BURSTS FROM PETER PARKER'S JACKET--

--STARTLING HIM NO LESS THAN THE BLACK CAT!

HEY!

YOU... WEBBED ME... BUT YOU DIDN'T EVEN *TRY* TO STOP HER! THAT MUST MEAN...

OH, SPIDER! I'M SO SORRY I DOUBTED YOU! CAN YOU EVER FORGIVE ME?

YEAH, SURE...

THAT WEBBING REALLY THREW ME!

THOUGH HIS JACKET RESEMBLES ORDINARY CLOTH, PETER PARKER KNOWS THAT IT IS SECRETLY AN ALIEN, BLACK COSTUME, ACQUIRED ON A DISTANT PLANET,* WHICH CAN ASSUME ANY APPEARANCE HE DESIRES...

I... NEVER REALIZED MY COSTUME COULD DO THAT--

* SEE THE MARVEL SUPER HEROES SECRET WARS LIMITED SERIES, ON SALE NOW-- DANNY.

--WHILE IT WAS STILL DISGUISED TO LOOK LIKE CIVVIES!

I'D BETTER BE MORE CAREFUL IN THE FUTURE!

I KNOW SO LITTLE ABOUT THIS COSTUME, AND ITS WEIRD ABILITIES--!

THAT TROUBLES ME, A LOT!

4

HEARTSDALE, NEW MEXICO...

WILL THAT BE ALL, MR. FIREHEART?

YES, WILLIS. PICK ME UP AT THE USUAL TIME.

THOMAS, YOU'RE BACK--! HOW WAS YOUR TRIP TO NEW YORK?

INTERESTING, BUT NOT QUITE AS SUCCESSFUL AS I'D HOPED. WHAT'S NEW HERE?

HHM! LET'S SEE...

THE GOVERNOR CALLED. HE'D LIKE AN APPOINTMENT THIS THURSDAY.

FINE!

ER... JENNA, BEFORE WE GET BOGGED DOWN WITH BUSINESS, I HAVE A JOB FOR YOU...

ASSEMBLE A DOSSIER ON THE NEW YORK VIGILANTE WHO GOES BY THE NAME OF SPIDER-MAN!

GET EVERYTHING YOU CAN ON HIM! I AM ESPECIALLY INTERESTED IN ANY FILMS WHICH SHOW HIM IN ACTION.

I UNDERSTAND, THOMAS.

I KNEW YOU WOULD,

I KNOW JENNA DOESN'T APPROVE OF MY ACTIVITIES AS PUMA, BUT THAT CAN'T BE HELPED. MY FIRST ENCOUNTER WITH SPIDER-MAN ENDED IN A STALEMATE. I INTEND TO BE BETTER PREPARED FOR OUR NEXT MEETING.

OUR NEXT AND FINAL MEETING!

5

MEANWHILE, AT 410 CHELSEA STREET...

THERE! THAT OUGHT TO KEEP OUT ANY MORE UNWANTED VISITORS!

BWAK! BWAK! BWAK!

PUMA REALLY DID A JOB ON THIS WINDOW!*

BWAK! BWAK!

WHICH BRINGS UP ANOTHER PROBLEM! THE GUY MAY NOT REALIZE THAT PETER PARKER IS SPIDER-MAN, BUT HE DOES KNOW WHERE I LIVE!

* SEE LAST ISSUE-- DANNY.

SO WHAT DO I DO-- *MOVE?!*

I CAN'T E'EN AFFORD THIS DIVE!

GUESS I OUGHT TO TRY MARY JANE AGAIN! THE LADY AND I HAVE TO TALK!

MOMENTS LATER, AT A FASHIONABLE UPPER WEST SIDE BROWNSTONE...

BRR-INGG!

BRR-INGG!

I WISH I COULD SAY GOODBYE TO YOU, PETER--

BRR-INGG!

--BUT IT'S BETTER FOR BOTH OF US IF I JUST QUIETLY VANISH OUT OF YOUR LIFE!

OH--!

THAT PHOTO MUST HAVE BEEN TANGLED UP WITHIN THIS BLOUSE!

GAYLE AND THE BOYS--!

OH, NO! IT'S HAPPENING ALL OVER AGAIN--!

I'M RUNNING OUT ON PETER JUST LIKE I RAN OUT ON MY OWN SISTER!

BRR-INGG!

WHY? WHY CAN'T I EVER STOP RUNNING?!

6

(NO ANSWER!) IT'S JUST AS WELL! WHAT WOULD I SAY TO HER ANYWAY?!

"HEY, *MJ*, IT'S ALL TRUE! I REALLY AM SPIDER-MAN, BUT YOU DON'T KNOW THE HALF OF IT..."

"NOT ONLY DO I POSSESS THE PROPORTIONATE STRENGTH, SPEED AND AGILITY OF A SPIDER, I EVEN OWN A WEIRDO COSTUME WHICH RESPONDS TO MY THOUGHTS AND HANGS ITSELF UP AT NIGHT--!"

YEAH, THAT WOULD REALLY WOW HER!

AW, WHAT'S THE USE? EVERYWHERE I LOOK, I SEE MORE AND MORE PROBLEMS...

MY AUNT MAY WON'T SPEAK TO ME BECAUSE I DROPPED OUT OF GRADUATE SCHOOL!

JOE ROBERTSON IS GIVING ME HASSLES AT WORK!

MY RELATIONSHIP WITH THE BLACK CAT SEEMS TO BE GETTING SHAKIER BY THE MOMENT!

AND, THERE'S A HOST OF BADDIES WHO'D JUST LOVE TO ACE ME!

≥ SHEESH≤ WHY DOES EVERYTHING HAVE TO BE SO COMPLICATED?

IT'S SO DEPRESSING! SOMETIMES I FEEL LIKE I HAVE ABSOLUTELY NO CONTROL OVER MY OWN LIFE!

THAT FRIGHTENS ME...

7

SOON, A TROUBLED SLEEP CLAIMS THE TIRED, BROODING YOUNG MAN. BUT, SHORTLY AFTER IT DOES...

...HIS UNCANNY COSTUME BEGINS TO STIR!

SERPENTLIKE, IT GLIDES ACROSS THE FLOOR, REACHING FOR HIM--

--FLOWING OVER HIM, UNTIL IT COVERS HIS ENTIRE BODY!

AND THEN...

AND YET, EVEN THOUGH SPIDER-MAN HAUNTS THIS NIGHT, AGILELY SPRING-ING FROM ROOFTOP TO ROOFTOP...

...IF WE COULD PEER BENEATH HIS MASK, WE WOULD SEE THAT PETER PARKER IS OBLIVIOUS TO ALL!

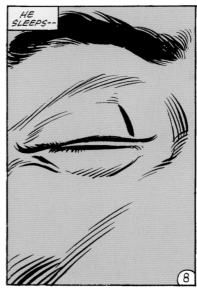

HE SLEEPS--

8

--AND DREAMS!

§GASP§

G-GOTTA KEEP RUNNING! CAN'T STOP--!

I CAN SENSE SOMETHING BEHIND ME! SOMETHING MONSTROUS!

IT'S GAINING ON ME! GETTING CLOSER--! *CLOSER*--!

ARGHH!

WAIT--! I CAN SEE IT BREAKING THROUGH THE MIST!

NO! IT CAN'T BE--! NOT YOU!

NOT YOU--!

SWAK!

WHA--? SOMETHING'S FORCING IT BACK! PUSHING IT AWAY--!

OH NO--!

IT... CAN'T BE!

PWAM!

I GOTTA GET AWAY FROM THESE MONSTERS BEFORE THEY KILL ME!

9

÷UGNN÷

NO! *NO!* LET ME GO!

STOP IT! *PLEASE--!* YOU'RE HURTING ME!

YOU'RE TEARING ME APART!

NOOOOO!

÷WHEW÷ TALK ABOUT *GRADE A* NIGHTMARES!

AND I LOOKED LIKE I DID IN HIGH SCHOOL--!

WISH I KNEW WHAT TO MAKE OF THAT!

HEY!

THAT DREAM MUST HAVE SPOOKED ME MORE THAN I REALIZED!

IT LOOKED LIKE MY COSTUME WAS MOVING JUST THEN--

--BUT I DIDN'T THINK IT COULD DO THAT WITHOUT AT LEAST SOME SORT OF MENTAL COMMAND FROM ME!

UH-OH! IT'S LATER THAN I THOUGHT! MUST BE LATE AFTERNOON!

LOOKS LIKE I SLEPT THROUGH ANOTHER DAY!

I'VE BEEN DOING THAT LATELY! IN FACT, I'VE BEEN DOING A LOT OF STRANGE THINGS...

WELL, I CAN'T KEEP LIVING ON THE EDGE LIKE THIS--!

I'VE JUST GOT TO GET MYSELF TOGETHER! GOT TO TAKE CHARGE OF MY LIFE!

AND, I'M GOING TO START BY GETTING SOME HARD ANSWERS ABOUT MY COSTUME...

10

AND SO, SOMETIME LATER...

THERE'S MY DESTINATION!

THE *BAXTER BUILDING*-- HEADQUARTERS OF THE *FANTASTIC FOUR!*

REED RICHARDS ONCE VOLUNTEERED TO ANALYZE MY COSTUME FOR ME!

BUT I JUST NEVER MADE THE TIME TO DROP IN ON HIM... UNTIL NOW!

HOPE HE'S HOME!

I WONDER IF I SHOULD HAVE PHONED AHEAD FOR AN APPOINT- MENT?

UNKNOWN TO SPIDER-MAN, *SCANNERS*- LOCATED ON THE BUILDING'S ROOFTOP-- ARE ALREADY AWARE OF HIS PRESENCE...

AND, ONCE THEY HAVE CON- FIRMED HIS IDENTITY...

THIS WINDOW SUDDENLY OPENED IN FRONT OF ME! AND SINCE I'M NOT GETTING ANY SPIDER- SENSE DANGER WARNING TINGLE...

...I MIGHT AS WELL TAKE AD- VANTAGE OF IT!

GREETINGS, SPIDER-MAN!

WHA--?! WHO ARE YOU?

I AM H.U.B.E.R.T.

MR. FANTASTIC AND THE HUMAN TORCH HAVE ALREADY BEEN NOTIFIED OF YOUR ARRIVAL. I SHALL ESCORT YOU TO THEM.

YEAH, THANKS.

I SHOULD HAVE REALIZED THAT *FF* HEADQUARTERS WOULD BE PRO- TECTED AGAINST SURPRISE VISITORS!

MOMENTS LATER...

YOU MAY ENTER THE THIRD LABORATORY ON THE LEFT. THEY ARE WAITING FOR YOU INSIDE.

WOW! THIS PLACE IS HUGE! AWESOME--!

HIYA, WEBS!

I'M SORRY THAT THE TORCH AND I COULDN'T BE THERE TO GREET YOU WHEN YOU ARRIVED, SPIDER-MAN, BUT WE WERE RIGHT IN THE MIDDLE OF A VERY IMPORTANT EXPERIMENT IN HEAT CONVERSION.

11

LONG TIME NO SEE, SPIDEY!

WHY THE UNEXPECTED VISIT?

I...ER...COULD USE SOME HELP, MATCHSTICK!

MY NEW COSTUME HAS BEEN ACTING KIND'A WEIRD LATELY, AND I WAS WONDERING IF...

NO PROBLEM, SON! I'D BE GLAD TO EX-AMINE IT FOR YOU!

IN FACT, I WAS HOPING YOU'D TAKE ME UP ON MY EARLIER OFFER!

JUST RELAX--! IT WILL ONLY TAKE ME A FEW MINUTES TO ASSEMBLE THE PROPER TESTING EQUIPMENT.

I DON'T WANT TO ALARM SPIDER-MAN UNNECESSARILY, BUT IF WHAT I SUSPECT IS TRUE... THIS COSTUME IS FAR MORE THAN IT APPEARS TO BE!

MOMENTS LATER, THE TESTS BEGIN...

HM! NO TRACE OF ANY MECHANICAL STRUCTURES!

WHERE CAN THAT WEBBING BE ORIGINATING FROM?

PWIP!

IT CAN APPARENTLY MIMIC ANY OUTWARD APPEARANCE THAT YOU CAN PICTURE IN YOUR MIND! FASCINATING--!

AND THE WAY IT FLOWS ON AND OFF YOUR BODY--! AMAZING!

12

MEANWHILE, ACROSS TOWN--

--AT THE PENTHOUSE APARTMENT OF THE CRIMINAL MASTERMIND KNOWN SIMPLY AS...THE ROSE!

MR. JOHNSTON! MR. VARLEY!

I WISH YOU TWO WOULD STOP GAWKING AT OUR GUEST.

IT IS RATHER RUDE.

YOU NEEDN'T STAND ON SUCH CEREMONY, ROSE! I'M QUITE USED TO PEOPLE STARING AT ME!

AFTER ALL, WHO WOULDN'T BE IMPRESSED BY--

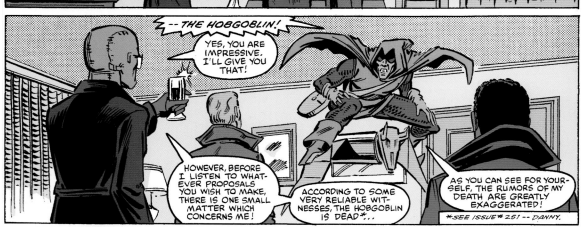

--THE HOBGOBLIN!

YES, YOU ARE IMPRESSIVE. I'LL GIVE YOU THAT!

HOWEVER, BEFORE I LISTEN TO WHATEVER PROPOSALS YOU WISH TO MAKE, THERE IS ONE SMALL MATTER WHICH CONCERNS ME!

ACCORDING TO SOME VERY RELIABLE WITNESSES, THE HOBGOBLIN IS DEAD*...

*SEE ISSUE #251 -- DANNY.

AS YOU CAN SEE FOR YOURSELF, THE RUMORS OF MY DEATH ARE GREATLY EXAGGERATED!

PERHAPS. AND YET, ANY MAN CAN DON A COSTUME...EVEN ONE AS OUTLANDISH AS YOURS.

I TRUST YOU WILL NOT OBJECT TO A LITTLE TEST.

BLZZAT!

13

A TEST? OH, COME NOW, ROSE... ONLY CHILDREN AND AMATEURS NEED TESTS... SO THAT THEY CAN PROVE THEIR SKILLS!

I AM THE HOBGOBLIN--

-- AND I WOULD FIND THIS WHOLE CHARADE INSULTING...

...WERE IT NOT SO AMUSING!

AARGH!

ENOUGH!

I AM SATISFIED THAT YOU ARE WHO YOU CLAIM TO BE!

I WOULD APPRECIATE IT IF YOU PUT THAT MAN DOWN GENTLY-- AND SPARED ME THE COST OF HIS HOSPITALIZATION!

FIVE SECONDS! HE TOOK OUT A HANDFUL OF OUR BEST MEN IN FIVE SECONDS! UNBELIEVABLE--!

NOW THEN, LET'S GET DOWN TO BUSINESS, SHALL WE?

I BELIEVE YOU HAVE A PROPOSITION...

I DO! ONE WHICH WILL HELP INCREASE YOUR POWER...UNTIL IT RIVALS THAT OF THE KINGPIN OF CRIME HIMSELF--

--WHILE, AT THE SAME TIME, IT ALSO INSURES THE DEATH OF OUR MUTUAL FOE... SPIDER-MAN!

14

MEANWHILE...

TELL ME, WEBS, DO YOU EVER THINK ABOUT THE BEYONDER'S PLANET?

SOMETIMES... LATE AT NIGHT...BUT I WISH I DIDN'T!

WHEN I REMEMBER WHAT GALACTUS HAD PLANNED TO DO TO US--!* WELL, I STILL GET THE SHAKES!

REFRESHMENTS, GENTLEMEN?

* SEE THE SECRET WARS--DANNY.

HEY--! THAT'S NEAT THE WAY YOUR COSTUME MELTS AWAY FROM YOUR MOUTH LIKE THAT!

YEAH, I JUST HOPE REED CAN EXPLAIN HOW IT DOES THESE TRICKS!

MAYBE HE'S GOT IT FIGURED OUT BY NOW. LET'S GO SEE...

HOW'S IT GOING, REED?

ALMOST THROUGH! JUST RECHECKING THIS DATA!

THESE RESULTS ARE ALMOST TOO STARTLING TO BELIEVE--!

SPIDER-MAN, UP UNTIL NOW, YOU'VE BEEN UNDER THE IMPRESSION THAT YOUR COSTUME IS COMPOSED OF AN ALIEN MATERIAL WHICH POSSESSES MANY RATHER UNIQUE ABILITIES...

UNFORTUNATELY, THIS ISN'T THE CASE!

YOU ARE WEARING A HIGHLY EVOLVED SYMBIOTE-- A SENTIENT BEING WHICH HAS ATTACHED ITSELF TO YOU BOTH MENTALLY AND PHYSICALLY!

YOU MEAN... IT'S ALIVE?!

15

YOU'RE KIDDING, RIGHT?!

THIS IS A GAG!?!

I'M AFRAID NOT! I SUGGEST YOU REMOVE IT IMMEDIATELY!

OKAY, SURE--

YEOW! I CAN'T--!

I'M ORDERING IT TO GET OFF ME-- BUT IT WON'T BUDGE!

IN FACT, IT'S GETTING TIGHTER! CRUSHING ME--!

OH, NO! IT'S JUST AS I FEARED--!

THE COSTUME IS AFRAID OF BEING SEPARATED FROM ITS HOST! IT'S ATTEMPTING TO PERMANENTLY GRAFT ITSELF TO SPIDER-MAN'S BODY!

WHAT SHOULD I DO, REED? TRY BURNING IT OFF HIM?

NO! THAT'S MUCH TOO DANGEROUS! YOU MIGHT SCORCH SPIDER-MAN IN THE PROCESS!

WE'LL HAVE TO TRY SOMETHING ELSE--!

WITHOUT ANOTHER WORD, MR. FANTASTIC STRETCHES HIS ARM DOWN A MAZE OF CORRIDORS--

16

-- UNTIL, UNERRINGLY, IT REACHES HIS GOAL--

--HIS SONIC BLASTER!

AND THEN...

ARE YOU SURE THIS IS GOING TO WORK?

NO, BUT WE CAN PRAY--!

HURRY! PLEASE--!

IT'S WORKING--! THE SONIC WAVES ARE DRIVING IT OFF SPIDER-MAN'S BODY!

GET READY, JOHNNY--!

I READ YOU LOUD AND CLEAR, BOSS-MAN!

FLAME ON!

THERE--! I'VE ENCIRCLED IT WITHIN A WALL OF FLAME!

GOOD WORK!

NOW, AS IT TRIES TO LEAP OVER THE FLAMES--

--ALL I HAVE TO DO IS SCOOP IT INTO THIS SPECIAL CONTAINER...

...WHICH CAN LATER BE PROGRAMMED TO DUPLICATE ITS ORIGINAL ALIEN ENVIRONMENT!

IF YOU SAY SO!

HEY, SPIDEY--

--WHY ARE YOU COVERING YOUR FACE? YOU CAN'T BE THAT UGLY!

GIVE ME A BREAK, TORCH!

YOU MAY NOT HAVE A SECRET IDENTITY, BUT I DO!

RELAX, SON! I'M CERTAIN THE TORCH CAN RUSTLE UP SOME-THING FOR YOU!

YEAH, LEAVE EVERYTHING TO ME!

HM--!

AND SHORTLY...

PREEEESENTING...THE ALL-NEW, TOTALLY REVAMPED SPIDER-MAN!

VERY FUNNY, FLAMEBRAIN! I'LL GET YOU FOR THIS--!

COULDN'T BE HELPED, WEBS! IT WAS EASY ENOUGH TO DIG UP AN OLD COSTUME FOR YOU TO SLIP INTO--

--BUT ⸮HEH HEH⸮ WE WERE A LITTLE SHORT ON MASKS...

17

KNOCK IT OFF, TORCH!

I STILL HAVE SOME IMPORTANT MATTERS TO DISCUSS WITH SPIDER-MAN!

I ASSUME THIS BELONGS TO YOU! IT MUST HAVE SLIPPED OUT OF YOUR COSTUME DURING ALL THE CONFUSION!

AS FOR THE "COSTUME" ITSELF...WELL, I THINK IT BEARS FURTHER INVESTIGATION...

SAY NO MORE--! YOU CAN HAVE IT!

WHY WOULD SPIDER-MAN CARRY A CAMERA?

I NEVER WANT TO SEE IT, AGAIN!

C'MON, SPIDEY! SINCE YOU CAN'T WEB-SWING YOUR WAY OUT OF HERE, I'LL GIVE YOU A LIFT TO A NEARBY ROOFTOP...

AND SO, SHORTLY...

ADIOS, AMIGO! I'M SURE YOU CAN GET HOME FROM HERE...WHEREVER IT IS THAT YOU CALL HOME!

I'LL MANAGE! THANKS FOR THE RIDE!

THINK NOTHING OF IT! ≥HEH HEH≤ I HAVEN'T HAD THIS MUCH FUN SINCE I PULLED MY LAST APRIL FOOL'S GAG ON THE THING!

WHAT A DAY! I'M SO BUMMED OUT ABOUT MY COSTUME THAT I CAN'T EVEN GET MAD AT THE TORCH!

A SYMBIOTE! WHAT COULD IT HAVE BEEN FEEDING OFF OF? GLANDULAR SECRETION? FAT CELLS? BODILY WASTES--?

≥BRRR≤ WHAT GRUESOME POSSIBILITIES--!--HEY! THIS COULD EXPLAIN WHY I'VE BEEN SO TIRED AND LISTLESS LATELY!

OH, NO!

AS IF I DIDN'T HAVE ENOUGH ON MY MIND, MY SPIDER-SENSE JUST STARTED A FOUR ALARM DANGER-BUZZ!

AND, I THINK I HEAR--

18

WHERE DID YOU COME FROM?

WHY ARE YOU HERE?

WHAT DO YOU CALL YOURSELF?

DO YOU HAVE ANY SUPER POWERS?

-POP- FLASH -POP-

WHAT'S THE SIGNIFICANCE OF THE PAPER BAG?

LET ME OUT OF HERE!

WOW! DID ANYONE CATCH THAT ON FILM? HE MUST HAVE LEAPED TWENTY-FIVE FEET STRAIGHT UP!

GOT TO GET AWAY--!

MINUTES LATER...

WHY ME? I CAN'T BELIEVE ALL THAT'S HAPPENED IN THE LAST TWENTY-FOUR HOURS!

MARY JANE ANNOUNCED THAT SHE'S ALWAYS KNOWN THAT I'M SPIDER-MAN! I HAVE AN ARGUMENT WITH THE BLACK CAT, AND A REAL DOOZIE OF A NIGHTMARE!

NOT ONLY DO I LEARN THAT MY COSTUME'S ALIVE, BUT I'M ALSO MADE THE BUTT OF ONE THE HUMAN TORCH'S SICK PRANKS!

AND NOW, I'VE BEEN TOTALLY HUMILIATED

WHAT MORE COULD GO WRONG?

WHAT THE--?!

SNOW!

SWELL! NOW, IT'S SNOWING....IN THE MIDDLE OF THE SUMMER!

I DON'T KNOW WHAT'S GOING ON. I DON'T WANT TO KNOW.* I JUST WANT TO GO HOME, AND FORGET THIS DAY EVER STARTED

*IF YOU'RE CURIOUS, DEAR READER, I SUGGEST YOU PICK UP A COPY OF THOR #349, ON SALE SOON --DANNY.

21

MUCH LATER...

...A SPOKESMAN FOR THE FANTASTIC FOUR DECLINED TO COMMENT TODAY ON THE SUDDEN APPEARANCE OF A NEW MASKED ADVENTURER! DUBBED THE "UNKNOWN SUPER HERO" BY THE PRESS--

-- HE WAS INSTRUMENTAL IN THE ARREST OF FOUR GUNMEN WHO WERE ALLEGEDLY ROBBING A LIQUOR STORE THIS AFTERNOON!

OFFICER WILLIAM SLATTERY, WHO WAS WOUNDED AT THE SCENE, IS PRESENTLY LISTED IN SATISFACTORY CONDITION...

DAY IN EVE WAY I AM GETTI BETTE AND BETTE BURMA S

GOOD! I'M GLAD TO HEAR HE'S DOING OKAY!

HMMM...

THESE OLD WEB-SHOOTERS ARE IN A SORRY STATE!

NOW THAT I'VE LOST MY BLACK COSTUME, IT'S GONNA TAKE ME AWHILE TO OUTFIT MYSELF AS SPIDER-MAN AGAIN...

LUCKILY, I STILL HAVE AN OLD RED AND BLUE COSTUME WHICH I CAN WEAR UNTIL... UH-OH!

KNOCK! KNOCK!

I'M COMING--!

MARY JANE--?!

HELLO, PETER. CAN I COME IN?

HAVE YOU SEEN THE WEATHER OUTSIDE? REAL WEIRD, HUH?

YEAH, BUT WE CAN TALK ABOUT THE WEATHER SOME OTHER TIME... I'VE, ER, BEEN TRYING TO CALL YOU!

I KNOW.

LOOK, PETER, I'M REAL SORRY I RAN OUT ON YOU YESTERDAY. IT WAS A ROTTEN THING TO DO.

MARY JANE, I...

NO, PETER. PLEASE LET ME FINISH... YOU SEE, I'VE BEEN DOING A LOT OF THINKING ABOUT YOU... ABOUT US... AND I'VE COME TO A DECISION.

I'VE KNOWN YOUR SECRETS FOR QUITE SOME TIME, BUT YOU'VE NEVER KNOWN MINE. WELL, I GUESS IT'S ONLY FAIR THAT YOU DO...

22

MEANWHILE...

IN A SECLUDED LABORATORY LOCATED WITHIN FANTASTIC FOUR HEADQUARTERS...

WHAM! WHAM! WHAM!

THE ALIEN ENTITY, WHICH HAD BEEN SPIDER-MAN'S COSTUME, HAMMERS AT ITS UNYIELDING PRISON...

WHAM!

WHAM!

AND, EVEN AS IT ASSESSES ITS CURRENT SITUATION, IT BEGINS TO PLAN--!

WHAM!

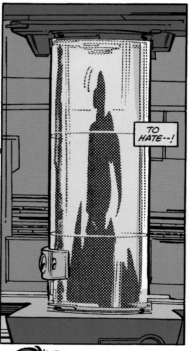

TO HATE--!

TO HUNGER FOR REVENGE--!

NEXT ISSUE!

MARY JANE WATSON REVEALS HER TRAGIC PAST!

PLUS-- THE HOBGOBLIN STRIKES! DON'T MISS...

"All My Pasts Remembered"!

I CARE ABOUT MARY JANE. I REALLY DO! HECK, I EVEN PROPOSED TO HER ONCE.

WHAT'S THE HARM IN HER KNOWING THAT I'M SPIDER-MAN?

BUT SHE CAN BE SO FLAKEY AT TIMES! CAN I REALLY TRUST HER WITH MY GREATEST SECRET?

RELAX, PETER! I KNOW WHAT YOU'RE THINKING ABOUT, AND YOU NEEDN'T WORRY.

I'M NOT THE SPACE CADET I APPEAR TO BE...

IT'S FUNNY, WE'VE KNOWN EACH OTHER FOR A LONG TIME...

...BUT WE REALLY DON'T *KNOW* EACH OTHER!

WE'RE SUPPOSED TO BE FRIENDS, BUT WE NEVER OPEN UP TO EACH OTHER. WE DON'T SHARE...

WE'RE A GREAT PAIR, AREN'T WE?

I GUESS I NEVER QUITE LOOKED AT IT LIKE THAT.

FRIENDSHIP CARRIES SOME PRETTY BIG RESPONSIBILITIES, BUT WE'VE JUST BEEN COASTING ALONG.

I DO THAT A LOT! SOMETIMES I THINK I'VE SPENT MY WHOLE LIFE RUNNING AWAY FROM THAT KIND OF RESPONSIBILITY.

I GUESS I GET THAT FROM MY PARENTS...

DID I EVER TELL YOU ABOUT THEM?

2

"THEY MET IN COLLEGE. MOM WAS A DRAMA STUDENT, AND DAD MAJORED IN MODERN AMERICAN LITERATURE.

"OH, THEY WERE SO IN LOVE IN THOSE DAYS! THEY JUST COULDN'T WAIT TO GET MARRIED.

"AFTER GRADUATION, MOM WANTED TO MOVE TO NEW YORK CITY, TO TRY HER HAND AT ACTING, BUT DAD HAD OTHER IDEAS...

BE SENSIBLE, MADELINE! I'VE ALREADY BEEN OFFERED A TEACHING POSITION, IT'S ONLY A SMALL COLLEGE OUT IN THE MIDDLE OF NOWHERE, BUT IT IS A START...

OH, PHILIP, I'D MOVE TO SIBERIA IF IT WOULD MAKE YOU HAPPY!

"THEY WERE MARRIED ABOUT EIGHTEEN MONTHS WHEN THEY HAD MY SISTER GAYLE...

"I WAS BORN FOUR YEARS LATER.

"AS THE YEARS PASSED, DAD BECAME A FULL PROFESSOR. HE WAS POPULAR WITH HIS STUDENTS, AND THE COLLEGE ADMINISTRATION RESPECTED HIM.

"MOM DEVOTED HER LIFE TO US KIDS

"MY PARENTS MUST HAVE LOOKED LIKE THEY HAD IT ALL...BUT DAD WASN'T SATISFIED. HE WANTED TO WRITE! TO PROVE TO THE WORLD THAT HE HAD THE SKILL AND TALENT TO BE ANOTHER FITZGERALD, A FAULKNER--!

"HE DIDN'T!

NO! NO! IT ISN'T COMING OUT RIGHT!

IT'S TRASH! EVERYTHING I WRITE IS TRASH!

CAN'T YOU KEEP THOSE KIDS QUIET?

MADELINE, IT'S YOUR FAULT I CAN'T CONCENTRATE!

HUSH, GIRLS! YOUR FATHER IS TRYING TO WORK!

BUT WE WEREN'T DOING ANYTHING, MOMMA!

I KNOW, SWEETHEART!

③

"DAD BEGAN SWITCHING JOBS, MOVING FROM ONE COLLEGE TO THE NEXT. I DON'T KNOW WHAT HE WAS LOOKING FOR, BUT HE NEVER SEEMED TO FIND IT.

"MOM ENDURED THE CONSTANT MOVING, EVEN THOUGH SHE HATED IT.

"I WASN'T WILD ABOUT IT EITHER.

"AS A RESULT, GAYLE AND I WERE ALWAYS CHANGING SCHOOLS. IT WASN'T EASY TO MAKE FRIENDS... BUT I REALLY WANTED THE OTHER KID'S TO LIKE ME, TO NOTICE ME...

WE HAVE A NEW STUDENT... MARY JANE WATSON.

THAT'S ME -- THE ONE AND ONLY!

"I GUESS I BECAME A BIT OF A CLASS CLOWN!

"GAYLE HANDLED HER LONELINESS DIFFERENTLY. SHE BEGAN TO STUDY DANCE...

"SHE WOULD PRACTICE FOR HOURS... JUST HER AND HER MUSIC!

"MEANWHILE, THINGS CONTINUED TO GET WORSE BETWEEN MOM AND DAD...

I NEVER WANTED A HOUSE OR CHILDREN!

THEY'RE ANCHORS HOLDING ME DOWN!

"AND THEN, ONE DAY...

ENOUGH! THOSE BLOODY DANCE LESSONS ARE COSTING ME A FORTUNE!

SWAK!

PHILIP, NO--!

NOT THE CHILDREN--! DON'T TAKE YOUR FRUSTRATIONS OUT ON THEM, TOO!

"I COULDN'T BELIEVE MY FATHER HAD ACTUALLY STRUCK GAYLE! I FELT HELPLESS! ENRAGED--!

"I DIDN'T KNOW WHAT TO DO, SO I BEGAN TO RUN...

HEY, MARY JANE! WHERE YOU GOING IN SUCH A HURRY?

YOU OKAY--? YOU LOOK LIKE SOMETHING'S WRONG!

W-WRONG--?!

ARE YOU KIDDING?

NOTHING'S EVER WRONG WITH MARY JANE WATSON!

4

"MOM FINALLY GAVE UP ON HER MARRIAGE A FEW WEEKS LATER, WHILE MY FATHER WAS BEING HONORED BY HIS COLLEGE..."

MAN OF THE YEAR

"WE SLIPPED OUT OF THE HOUSE WHILE HE WAS STILL AT THE AWARDS CEREMONY. I GUESS MOM JUST COULDN'T FACE HIM ANYMORE..."

"A MESSY DI-VORCE FOLLOWED! DAD SUED HER FOR DESERTION, AND THE COURT WASN'T VERY SYMPATHETIC TOWARDS HER..."

"WE DIDN'T HAVE MUCH MONEY, SO WE WERE FORCED TO TURN TO FAMILY FOR HELP..."

I STILL DON'T SEE WHY WE'VE GOT TO TAKE THEM IN!

THEY'RE KIN, AND THEY'VE GOT NO - WHERE ELSE TO GO!

"IT WASN'T EASY ON US, BEING SHUFFLED FROM ONE SET OF RELATIVES TO ANOTHER, BUT I TRIED TO MAKE THE MOST OUT OF IT..."

OH, DOLLINK! YOU'RE SO CUTE, I COULD DIIIE!

≈GIGGLE≈ THAT'S A GREAT AUNT MARTHA, MARY JANE!

"IT'S FUNNY, BUT THERE WAS ONLY ONE RELATIVE THAT I ENJOYED VISITING. MY FATHER'S SISTER... AUNT ANNA! SHE ALWAYS MADE ME FEEL SO AT HOME--!"

MARY JANE, I WANT YOU TO MEET MY FRIEND MAY PARKER!

SHE HAS A NEPHEW WHO'S ONLY A YEAR OLDER THAN YOU!

"I MUST HAVE BEEN AROUND THIR-TEEN WHEN I FIRST LAID EYES ON YOU, PETER! YOU WERE JUST STARTING HIGH SCHOOL, AND YOU LOOKED SO SERIOUS! A REAL BOOKWORM!"

"DO YOU REMEMBER HOW OUR AUNTS WERE ALWAYS TRYING TO GET US TOGETHER?"

"DO YOU PETER?"

"PETER--?"

HOW COULD I EVER FORGET?

⑤

AUNT MAY WAS ALWAYS TRYING TO SET ME UP WITH ANNA WATSON'S NIECE, BUT I STILL MANAGED TO PUT OFF MEETING YOU FOR YEARS!

FOOLISH BOY!

DON'T BLAME ME! I WAS ONLY TOLD THAT YOU HAD A GREAT PERSONALITY, AND YOU KNOW WHAT *THAT* MEANS!

WHEN I THINK OF ALL THE TIME I WASTED AVOIDING YOU--!

THAT'S THE TROUBLE WITH TIME, PETER! IT HAS A NASTY HABIT OF SLIPPING AWAY FROM US...

ELSEWHERE, AT THAT VERY MOMENT...

LET'S GO, GUYS! HURRY IT UP!

I SPENT A SMALL FORTUNE CONVERTING THESE STUPID TRAINS--

--INTO THE CITY'S CLASSIEST CASINO, AND I DON'T WANT ANYTHING GOING WRONG ON OPENING NIGHT!

YOU NEEDN'T WORRY, MR. HUDSON!

THE COPS WOULD NEVER THINK OF LOOKING FOR AN OPERATION LIKE THIS IN A "DESERTED" TRAIN YARD!

KA-BWAMM!

WHAT THE--?!

THE ROOF--! SOMETHING'S BLASTING A HOLE IN OUR ROOF!

ELSEWHERE...

WHATEVER HAPPENED TO YOUR FATHER?

HE MOVED TO OREGON SOME YEARS AGO... AND HE DIDN'T EVEN BOTHER TO SAY GOOD-BYE.

I WROTE TO HIM A FEW TIMES, BUT HE NEVER ANSWERED MY LETTERS.

AFTER A WHILE, I STOPPED TRYING...

"MEANWHILE, MOM HAD FINALLY FOUND US A PERMANENT PLACE TO LIVE... WITH HER COUSIN, FRANK BROWN!

"FRANK WAS A STEEL WORKER WHOSE WIFE HAD DIED THE YEAR BEFORE...

"HE TOOK US IN ON THE CONDITION THAT MOM WOULD KEEP HOUSE FOR HIM, AND HIS THREE CHILDREN...

"LIVING WITH FRANK WAS QUITE AN EXPERIENCE. HE WAS A HARD MAN. STERN! UNFORGIVING! BUT, HE DID TREAT US FAIRLY--

"--AND, HE BROUGHT A CERTAIN AMOUNT OF STABLITY TO OUR LIVES. THAT'S WHEN GAYLE FIRST STARTED DATING TIMMY... *TIMMY BYRNES!*

"OH, HE WAS SUCH A HUNK IN HIGH SCHOOL. I WAS HALF IN LOVE WITH HIM MYSELF.

"I REMEMBER HOW HAPPY GAYLE WAS! EVERYTHING WAS FINALLY COMING TO-GETHER FOR HER!

"HER DANCE TEACHER WAS CERTAIN SHE HAD A REAL SHOT AT A COLLEGE SCHOLARSHIP.

"SHE WAS LIVING EVERY YOUNG GIRL'S FANTASY! NOT ONLY WAS HER BOYFRIEND THE CAPTAIN OF THE FOOTBALL TEAM--

"-- BUT HE WAS ONE OF THE SCHOOL'S TOP SCHOLAR'S, TOO!

THE NATIONAL HONOR SOCIETY WELCOMES TIMOTHY BYRNES TO ITS RANKS!

"YEAH, THINGS LOOKED GREAT! IT'S A SHAME FANTASIES DON'T WORK OUT IN REAL LIFE...

8

"GAYLE KEPT STUDYING, AND WORKING AT HER ART!"

"SHE LOVED TO DANCE! SHE REALLY DID!"

"BUT, IT WAS REAL OBVIOUS THAT SHE LOVED TIMMY EVEN MORE!"

"AS FOR ME, I WAS BUSY WITH THE SCHOOL'S DRAMA DEPARTMENT...

JULIET! WHEREFORE ART THOU?

HERE I AM, TIGER!

HA HA HA

"NEEDLESS TO SAY, MY FIRST FEW PERFORMANCES LACKED A CERTAIN 'POLISH'...

"AS THE SCHOOL YEAR DREW TO A CLOSE, GAYLE DROPPED HER BIG BOMB...

TIMMY AND I HAVE DECIDED TO GET MARRIED AS SOON AS WE GRADUATE HIGH SCHOOL!

WHAT--?

ARE YOU CRAZY?! YOU'RE THROWING AWAY YOUR CHANCE FOR COLLEGE! FOR EVERYTHING--!

YOU CAN'T TELL ME HOW TO LIVE MY LIFE, MOM--

--NOT AFTER THE MESS YOU MADE OF YOURS!

"IN THE END, GAYLE HAD HER WAY...

"THEY WERE MARRIED IN A SIMPLE CHURCH CEREMONY.

"SOON AFTER THAT THEY LEFT TOWN. TIMMY PLANNED TO ENTER A PRE-LAW COLLEGE PROGRAM IN THE FALL, AND GAYLE WAS GOING TO TAKE A JOB TO HELP SUPPORT THEM...

"FOR SOME CRAZY REASON, THAT SEEMED VERY ROMANTIC TO ME AT THE TIME.

"PRETTY DUMB, HUH?

"THE NEXT YEAR WAS A WILD TIME FOR ME. I WAS FIFTEEN, AND LIFE WAS BEAUTIFUL! I EVEN ACTED IN A FEW MORE PLAYS...

I HAVE ALWAYS DEPENDED ON THE KINDNESS OF STRANGERS!

"IT WASN'T BAD!

"AND THEN, I RECEIVED THE LETTER...

IT'S FROM GAYLE! SHE'S COMING TO VISIT. SHE HAS A SURPRISE FOR US!

I WONDER WHAT IT IS?

9

"WHEN THEY ARRIVED, WE FOUND OUT...

OH, GAYLE, I'M SO HAPPY FOR YOU AND TIM!

YEAH, EVERYONE WAS HAPPY FOR THEM!

"WELL, *ALMOST* EVERYONE...

"I STILL REMEMBER THE DAY THE BABY WAS BORN! HE WAS THE CUTEST LITTLE BOY--!

"BUT THE EXPRESSION ON TIMMY'S FACE--! HE WAS ONLY NINETEEN, BUT HE LOOKED SO HAGGARD. SO DESPERATE! LIKE SOME CAGED ANIMAL--"

--OR A DROWNING MAN WHO HAD JUST BEEN TOSSED AN ANCHOR!

C'MON, MARY JANE, IT COULDN'T HAVE BEEN *THAT* BAD! I THOUGHT HE LOVED YOUR SISTER.

HE DID, BUT THAT DIDN'T CHANGE THE FACTS...

TIMMY HAD BARELY FINISHED HIS FIRST YEAR OF COLLEGE!

HE LOVED GAYLE! I'M SURE HE DID--! BUT THAT DIDN'T MEAN HE COULD ACCEPT THE RESPONSIBILITY FOR RAISING A FAMILY!

TRUE LOVE... *HA!*

IT DOESN'T STAND A CHANCE AGAINST REALITY!

WHAT GOOD IS IT, ANYWAY?!

10

MEANWHILE, JUST BEYOND CENTRAL PARK...

...A SMALL, UPPER WEST SIDE CONFECTIONARY STANDS.

AND, INSIDE THE BUSY STORE...

KEEP AN EYE ON THE PLACE, FELLAS!

I'LL BE IN THE BACK IN CASE ANYBODY NEEDS ME.

HOW WE DOING, BOSS?

THE AFTERNOON TALLY LOOKS PRETTY GOOD SO FAR!

BETTER PLACE YOUR BETS, BOYS! THE NEXT RACE STARTS IN TWO MINUTES...

BWOOOM!

SAVE YOUR MONEY, GENTLEMEN!

THERE WILL ONLY BE ONE WINNER TODAY!

AND HIS NAME IS... HOBGOBLIN!

BWAKK!

WHAT ARE YOU CLOWNS WAITING FOR--AN ENGRAVED INVITATION?!

SMASH THAT FLYING FREAK BEFORE HE WRECKS THE PLACE!

YOU HEARD MR. SANTELLIO! GET 'IM!

WE'LL TACKLE HIM ALL AT ONCE!

11

12

MEANWHILE...

YOU OKAY?

YEAH... I GUESS SO.

I WAS JUST THINKING ABOUT TIMMY BYRNES...

HE REALLY WASN'T SUCH A BAD GUY.

I DON'T THINK HE EVER MEANT TO HURT GAYLE, OR ANYONE ELSE.

HE WAS JUST A KID WHO LET HIS LIFE GET OUT OF HIS CONTROL.

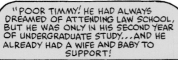

"POOR TIMMY! HE HAD ALWAYS DREAMED OF ATTENDING LAW SCHOOL, BUT HE WAS ONLY IN HIS SECOND YEAR OF UNDERGRADUATE STUDY... AND HE ALREADY HAD A WIFE AND BABY TO SUPPORT!

"THINK OF THE STRAIN HE MUST HAVE BEEN UNDER! THE PRESSURE--!

"NO WONDER HIS GRADES BEGAN TO SLIP...AND HIS MARRIAGE BEGAN TO FAIL!

YOU'RE THE REASON I CAN'T STUDY PROPERLY!

YOU AND YOUR KID!

"GAYLE WAS CONFUSED! DESPERATE! SHE STARTED CALLING MOM FOR ADVICE, FOR SUPPORT--! BUT THAT LED TO OTHER ARGUMENTS...

GET OFF THE PHONE, MADELINE!

LET THE KIDS SOLVE THEIR OWN PROBLEMS!

FRANK, PLEASE--! MY DAUGHTER NEEDS ME!

"MAYBE UNCLE FRANK WAS RIGHT! MAYBE MY MOTHER SHOULDN'T HAVE GOTTEN SO INVOLVED! SHE HADN'T BEEN FEELING WELL FOR MONTHS, AND THOSE PHONE CALLS CERTAINLY WEREN'T DOING HER ANY GOOD.

"I KNOW I TRIED TO SHUT GAYLE AND TIMMY OUT OF MY MIND...

"I WAS ONLY IN HIGH SCHOOL! PROMS AND PARTIES--THAT'S ALL I WANTED TO THINK ABOUT!

"BUT THEN, GAYLE CALLED WITH A RATHER STARTLING ANNOUNCEMENT...

MOM, I...I'M PREGNANT, AGAIN!

THAT'S WONDERFUL, SWEETHEART!

"MOM STILL WASN'T IN THE BEST OF HEALTH, BUT SHE DECIDED TO CELEBRATE GAYLE'S NEWS WITH A SURPRISE VISIT! SHE TRULY BELIEVED THAT A SECOND CHILD WOULD FORCE TIMMY TO ACCEPT HIS RESPONSIBILITIES, WOULD HEAL THE MARRIAGE! BUT...

GAYLE, WHAT'S WRONG? WHERE'S TIMOTHY?

HE'S...GONE! PACKED HIS BAGS AND LEFT.

SAID HE COULDN'T COPE WITH THE THOUGHT OF ANOTHER CHILD!

13

"I SUPPOSE I SHOULD HAVE HATED TIMMY FOR WHAT HE'D DONE TO GAYLE... BUT I COULDN'T! NOT WHEN I WANTED TO RUN AWAY, TOO!"

DON'T WORRY, DEAR! YOUR SISTER AND I WON'T DESERT YOU! I'LL PHONE YOUR UNCLE FRANK, AND TELL HIM WE'RE STAYING HERE!

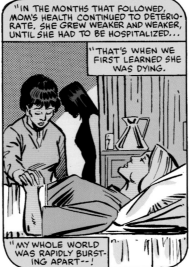

"IN THE MONTHS THAT FOLLOWED, MOM'S HEALTH CONTINUED TO DETERIORATE. SHE GREW WEAKER AND WEAKER, UNTIL SHE HAD TO BE HOSPITALIZED..."

"THAT'S WHEN WE FIRST LEARNED SHE WAS DYING."

"MY WHOLE WORLD WAS RAPIDLY BURSTING APART--!"

"TO HELP WITH THE BILLS, I DROPPED ALL MY EXTRACURRICULAR ACTIVITIES-- INCLUDING DRAMA CLUB-- AND DEVOTED MYSELF TO A SERIES OF AFTER-SCHOOL JOBS..."

"WITH ALL HER GRIEF, MY MOM STILL HAD ONE LAST DREAM. SHE WAS DETERMINED TO LIVE LONG ENOUGH TO SEE HER SECOND GRANDCHILD."

"SHE... DIDN'T MAKE IT."

I KNOW THINGS LOOK PRETTY BAD NOW, MARY JANE, BUT WE'LL FIND A WAY TO MAKE THINGS WORK OUT. TRUST ME--!

ONCE I HAVE THIS BABY, I'LL GET A FULL-TIME JOB...AND YOU WON'T HAVE TO WORK SO HARD AFTER SCHOOL!

WE CAN FIND SOMEONE TO WATCH THE KIDS DURING THE DAY, AND--

NO.

NO!

YOUR KIDS ARE YOUR PROBLEM! I'VE GOT MY OWN LIFE TO LIVE--AND I'M NOT GOING TO WASTE IT, LIKE MOM WASTED HERS!

YOU AND MOM-- AND EVEN TIMMY-- GAVE UP YOUR DREAMS BECAUSE YOU WANTED TO MAKE SOMEONE ELSE HAPPY!

WELL, THAT'S NOT GOING TO HAPPEN TO ME!

MARY JANE, WAIT--!

NO! I WANT MORE OUT OF LIFE! MUCH MORE!

"POOR GAYLE! I NEVER LOOKED BACK AT HER. I JUST STARTED RUNNING...!"

14

...AND, IN ONE WAY OR ANOTHER, I'VE BEEN RUNNING EVER SINCE!

IT'S ALMOST BEEN FOUR YEARS SINCE I LAST SAW MY SISTER, HER SECOND CHILD WAS ANOTHER BABY BOY...

CUTE LITTLE GUY, TOO! AUNT ANNA SHOWED ME PICTURES WHEN HE WAS BORN.

I ONLY WISH MOMMA COULD HAVE LIVED TO SEE HIM...

WHY DON'T *YOU* GO SEE HIM? MAYBE YOU AND YOUR SISTER COULD FINALLY COME TO TERMS.

I DON'T THINK THAT'S POSSIBLE, PETER. TOO MUCH TIME HAS PASSED...

I'VE PHONED GAYLE A FEW TIMES OVER THE YEARS... MOSTLY ON HOLIDAYS AND THE KIDS' BIRTHDAYS. SHE'S NEVER HAPPY TO HEAR FROM ME.

I DON'T THINK SHE'S EVER FORGIVEN ME FOR DESERTING HER.

I REALLY DON'T BLAME HER! I'VE NEVER FORGIVEN MYSELF, EITHER.

MY AUNT MAY ONCE TOLD ME THAT MARY JANE AND I HAD A LOT IN COMMON. WE'VE BOTH LOST...SO VERY MUCH.

AUNT MAY... I'VE EVEN LOST *HER* RECENTLY! SHE HASN'T SPOKEN TO ME SINCE I TOLD HER THAT I HAD DROPPED OUT OF GRADUATE SCHOOL!

I REALLY SHOULD HAVE STRAIGHTENED THINGS OUT BETWEEN US LONG BEFORE NOW, BUT I'VE JUST BEEN SO BUSY LATELY. I JUST HOPE I HAVEN'T LET TOO MUCH TIME PASS...

AND, I STILL DON'T WHAT TO DO ABOUT MARY JANE KNOWING MY SECRET IDENTITY. THE GIRL JUST BARED HER SOUL TO ME! HOW CAN I LIE TO HER NOW?!

I REALLY DIDN'T MEAN TO LAY ALL MY GRIEF ON YOU, PETER. IT JUST SORT OF CAME OUT.

YOU'RE A GOOD LISTENER.

15

JUST THEN, AT THE *BAXTER BUILDING,* WORLD FAMOUS HEADQUARTERS OF THE *FANTASTIC FOUR...*

HEY, REED...

...I FINALLY MANAGED TO DISCONNECT THIS MODULE FROM YOUR OLD PARTICLE ACCELERATOR. WHERE DOES IT GO NOW?

REED--?

YOO-HOO!

OH, HELLO, SHE-HULK. I'LL BE WITH YOU IN A MOMENT...

GEE, I HOPE I'M NOT INTERRUPTING AN IMPORTANT EXPERIMENT.

NOT AT ALL! I WAS JUST USING MY THOUGHT TRANSMITTER--

--IN AN ATTEMPT TO ESTABLISH CONTACT WITH THIS ALIEN ENTITY. BUT, SO FAR, I'VE BEEN UNSUCCESSFUL.

YOU PROBABLY DON'T RECOGNIZE IT IN THIS FORM, BUT SPIDER-MAN BROUGHT IT BACK WITH HIM FROM THE BEYONDER'S PLANET.* UP UNTIL RECENTLY, HE WAS WEARING IT AS HIS COSTUME...

...BUT THEN, I EXAMINED IT, AND DISCOVERED THAT IT WAS, IN FACT, A LIVING CREATURE...

*SEE THE MARVEL SUPER HEROES SECRET WARS LIMITED SERIES FOR DETAILS --DANNY

...A *SYMBIOTE* THAT WAS DETERMINED TO PERMANENTLY GRAFT ITSELF TO THE WEB-SWINGER'S BODY!*

÷WHEW÷ AND I USED TO THINK IT LOOKED SEXY ON HIM!

*AS RELATED LAST ISSUE -- DANNY, AGAIN!

WHAT MAKES YOU THINK YOU CAN COMMUNICATE WITH IT?

JUST A HUNCH, REALLY. IT USED TO RESPOND TO SPIDER-MAN'S THOUGHTS.

THAT COULD IMPLY A CERTAIN LEVEL OF INTELLIGENCE.

GIVE ME A BREAK! NEXT, YOU'LL BE TELLING ME THAT IT'S CAPABLE OF FEELING EMOTIONS. LIKE LOVE...

...AND HATE!

MEANWHILE, ACROSS TOWN...

YOU HAVE DONE WELL, MY FRIEND!

WITHIN A FEW WEEKS, WE WILL CONTROL ALL OF THE MAJOR GAMBLING INTERESTS IN THIS CITY.

EXACTLY! I TOLD YOU MY PLAN WAS FOOL-PROOF!

WITH YOUR INSIDER'S KNOWLEDGE OF THE RACKETS AND MY POWER, NOTHING CAN STOP US!

I TRUST YOU HAVEN'T FORGOTTEN ABOUT THE KINGPIN OF CRIME.

HE WILL NOT BE PLEASED WHEN HE LEARNS THAT THE HOBGOBLIN HAS JOINED FORCES WITH THE ROSE!

WE WILL DEAL WITH THE KINGPIN IN DUE TIME!

BUT NOW I AM MUCH MORE CONCERNED WITH A MATTER OF PERSONAL VENGEANCE. I WOULD LIKE TO BORROW A FEW OF YOUR MEN!

I WANT THEM TO PAY A BUSINESS CALL ON SOME OLD FRIENDS OF MINE...

...MR. AND MRS. HARRY OSBORN!

18

TWO HOURS LATER...

IT'S A SHAME MARY JANE HAD A DATE TONIGHT! WE WERE GETTING ALONG SO WELL! I WONDER IF WE COULD EVER--

WHOA! I DON'T LIKE THE DIRECTION THAT THOUGHT WAS TAKING!

I'M ALREADY IN LOVE WITH THE BLACK CAT! I SHOULDN'T EVEN BE THINKING ABOUT MARY JANE IN THAT LIGHT,...BUT I CAN'T SEEM TO HELP MYSELF!

WHY CAN'T ROMANCE EVER BE SIMPLE?

BAH! I CAN'T WORRY ABOUT MY SCREWED UP LOVE LIFE NOW!

IF THIS AFTERNOON CONVINCED ME OF ANYTHING, IT'S THAT I'VE GOT TO MAKE PEACE BETWEEN ME AND AUNT MAY BEFORE ANYMORE TIME PASSES!

I'LL SEE HER TONIGHT!

KLICK

MIGHT AS WELL CATCH THE EVENING NEWS WHILE I CHANGE CLOTHES.

EH--?!

÷SPUTTER÷...HAD BATTLED THE MYSTERIOUS SPIDER-MAN ON MANY OCCASIONS! UP UNTIL RECENTLY, THE AUTHORITIES BELIEVED HIM DEAD--

-- BUT NEW EVIDENCE SEEMS TO INDICATE OTHERWISE! THE HOBGOBLIN MAY WELL BE ALIVE!

NUMEROUS EYEWITNESSES CLAIMED TO HAVE SEEN HIM GLIDING OVER THIS CITY'S ROOFTOPS EARLIER THIS AFTERNOON!

THE HOBGOBLIN--! I NEVER REALLY BELIEVED HE DIED THE LAST TIME WE FOUGHT!*

I'VE BEEN WAITING FOR THIS--! I ALWAYS KNEW I'D HAVE TO FACE HIM, AGAIN!

* SEE ISSUE #251--DANNY!

19

THIS WEB-SHOOTER CHECKS OUT FINE!

SO DOES THIS ONE! I EVEN LOADED THEM WITH FRESH WET-FLUID CARTRIDGES, SO I WON'T HAVE TO WORRY ABOUT RUNNING LOW ON WEBBING!

I CAN'T BE TOO CAREFUL WHEN IT COMES TO HOBGOBLIN! HE'S ONE OF THE MOST DANGEROUS FOES I'VE EVER FOUGHT!

HE'S GOT AN ARSENAL OF DEADLY WEAPONS AT HIS COMMAND!

HIS SUPER-STRENGTH IS NEARLY THE EQUAL OF MY OWN!

AND, I'VE NEVER MET ANYONE HALF AS CUNNING--!

HE'S ALWAYS MANAGED TO FIGHT ME TO A DRAW IN THE PAST!

NOT THIS TIME!

21

EPILOG:

NEW YORK, NEW YORK. THE BAXTER BUILDING STANDS, NOW, SILENT AND EMPTY.

BUT NOT AT PEACE.

SLIPPING WITH CARELESS EASE PAST A HUNDRED ALARM SENSORS A TINY DEVICE MOVES THROUGH THE DESERTED HALLS.

HERE AND THERE IT PAUSES, A MICRO-DRILL BORING INVISIBLY SMALL HOLES IN THE MANY COMPLEX MECHANISMS, INSERTING STRANGE COMPONENTS...

...ALTERING.

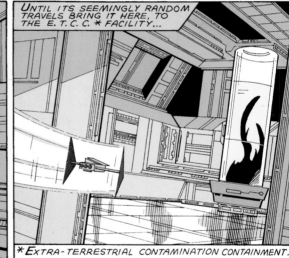

UNTIL ITS SEEMINGLY RANDOM TRAVELS BRING IT HERE, TO THE E.T.C.C. * FACILITY...

*EXTRA-TERRESTRIAL CONTAMINATION CONTAINMENT.

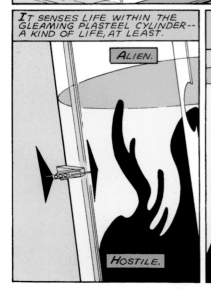

IT SENSES LIFE WITHIN THE GLEAMING PLASTEEL CYLINDER-- A KIND OF LIFE, AT LEAST.

ALIEN.

HOSTILE.

AND SOMETHING ELSE. SOMETHING THAT TOUCHES AGAINST ITS MICRO-CIRCUITS LIKE THE TICKLE OF TINY, ELFIN FINGERS.

AS IF SOMEONE...SOMETHING WERE TRYING TO... MAKE A SUGGESTION?

THE FAINT PROMPTING HAS NO EFFECT, BUT IT DOES SEEM WORTH FURTHER INVESTIGATION...

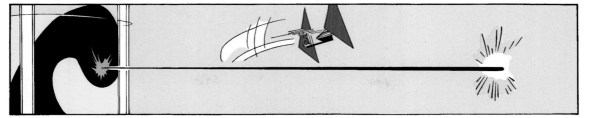

NEXT ISSUE: *SHE HULK IS ONE LADY YOU'D RATHER HAVE FOR YE THAN* **AGIN'** *YE-- AS A CERTAIN SLEAZOID PUBLISHER FINDS OUT IN...* **THE NAKED TRUTH** *BE HERE IN 30 DAYS!!*

Back in his old red and blue suit, and feeling better than ever after ridding himself of the alien parasite, Spider-Man continues to hunt, and eventually defeat, the Hobgoblin.

But even out of his mask, Peter Parker still has his fair share of problems. Though he reconciles his friendship with Mary Jane, his Aunt May refuses to talk to him, furious at Peter for dropping out of college.

His personal life takes a further twist when he discovers that the Kingpin was behind the Black Cat's new powers. Coupled with the fact that she seemed to only care about Spider-Man and not Peter Parker, he ends their relationship. However, Peter is unaware that the Cat was about to break-up with him anyway before her bad luck powers accidentally killed him.

Meanwhile, the liberated alien symbiote continues to skulk and slither through the shadows of New York, eventually creeping all the way back to Peter Parker's apartment...

LOUISE SIMONSON • WRITER
GREG LaROCQUE • PENCILLER
JIM MOONEY • INKER
JANICE CHIANG • LETTERER
GEORGE ROUSSOS • COLORIST
DANNY FINGEROTH & JIM OWSLEY • EDITORS
JIM SHOOTER • EDITOR-IN-CHIEF
'TIL DEATH DO US PART!
I'M JUST BEING PARANOID!
THAT'S GOTTA BE IT! I JUST BROKE UP WITH THE BLACK CAT*, AND EVEN IF WE BOTH KNOW IT'S FOR THE BEST, SHE'S FURIOUS WITH ME!
IT'S COLORING MY WHOLE OUTLOOK! THAT'S WHY I'VE GOT THIS FUNNY FEELING... ALMOST LIKE SOMEBODY'S OUT TO GET ME!
OOH, BAMBI! LIKE, IT'S SO COLD OUT HERE! BUT... THE SUN LOOKED SO WARM!
IT'S THE GIRLS NEXT DOOR... UP ON THE ROOF AGAIN! RATS!
* IT HAPPENED IN PETER PARKER #100 A COLLECTOR'S ITEM FOR SURE! -- OWZ.

BRRR! NOBODY SUNBATHES IN WEATHER LIKE *THIS*, RANDI! NOT EVEN *US*!

YEAH, BAMBI! LET'S GET BACK INSIDE! *FAST!*

SO...THOSE NUTTY TEEN-AGE SUNBUNNIES HAVE *FINALLY* REALIZED IT'S AUTUMN!

TOOK THEM LONG ENOUGH! THEY *MUST* BE YOUNG! AND RIGHT NOW I'M FEELING AS OLD AS METHUSALA!

WHAT YOU NEED, *PETER PARKER*, IS A NICE JAUNT AROUND TOWN...

...COURTESY OF YOUR FRIENDLY NEIGHBORHOOD *SPIDER-MAN!* SHAKE LOOSE THE COBWEBS! PERK YOU RIGHT UP!

HEY, I MUST BE GETTING USED TO MY OLD RED AND BLUE COSTUME AGAIN!

FEELS AS COMFORTABLE AS THE SHAPE-SHIFTING *BLACK* ONE I GOT ON THE SECRET WARS...

...THE ONE THAT TURNED OUT TO BE AN *ALIEN SYMBIOT!*

I'D WORN IT TO THE BAXTER BUILDING TO VISIT THE *FANTASTIC FOUR*...

...AND *REED RICHARDS* EXAMINED IT...AND DISCOVERED IT WAS A LIVING *PARASITE*-- AND THAT IT WAS TRYING TO GRAFT ITSELF ON- TO ME!

AND IT REFUSED TO COME OFF! HOO BOY! REED FINALLY MADE IT LET GO BY BLASTING IT WITH A *SONIC GUN!*

HE SAID IT WAS JUST A *MATTER OF TIME* BEFORE IT TOOK ME OVER COMPLETELY!

WONDER WHAT HE MEANT BY *THAT?*

I GUESS WHAT'S REALLY WORRYING ME ARE THE RUMORS ABOUT A *BLACK SHADOW* SNAKING AROUND TOWN AND TAKING PEOPLE OVER!

MAYBE I SHOULD CALL REED, JUST TO MAKE SURE MY ALIEN COSTUME'S STILL *LOCKED AWAY!*

AW! SURE IT IS! THE FF DON'T KNOW MY SECRET IDENTITY, BUT IF IT *HAD* ESCAPED, THEY'D HAVE CONTACTED ME SOMEHOW...

...*WOULDN'T* THEY?

EMPTY! GOTTA ADD NEW WEB FLUID TO MY WEB SHOOTERS AND...

OLYMPIC XXI

HEY, WHERE'S MY CARTRIDGE BELT? AND MY HOOD AND GLOVES? PROBABLY DROPPED INTO THE BOTTOM OF THE CLOSET!

DARN! SERVES YOU RIGHT, PARKER, FOR HANGING IT UP, INSTEAD OF THROWING IT ON THE CHAIR AS USUAL!

I STILL HAVE THIS FUNNY FEELING, THOUGH! THINK I'LL *VISIT* REED SOON AS I'M DRESSED!

JUST TO MAKE *SURE!*

OH...

NO!

WHILE IN MANHATTAN'S *LOWER EAST SIDE...*

WHY, *GRIPES,* GUESS WHAT *DAY* THIS IS? AND THIS LOVELY LADY WALKING HOME FROM THE BANK ALL *ALONE...?*

NO FOOLIN', *SUGAR FACE?* IT'S *SOCIAL SECURITY CHECK DAY?*

C-COME ON, *G-GUYS! DON'T!* YOU'LL S-SPOIL EVERYTHING! SOME-BODY'LL S-SEE!

GIMME A BREAK, *PIGEON!*

NO! P-PLEASE! HOW'LL I BUY FOOD? PAY THE RENT?

THAT'S ALL THE MONEY I HAVE IN THE WORLD!

NOT ANY *MORE,* BABE!

BUT S-SUGAR FACE! GRIPES! LISTEN TO ME!

W-WITH THE *BANK ROBBERY* WE JUST PULLED USING OUR *W-WINGS,* WE DON'T *NEED* TO M-MUG PEOPLE ANY M-MORE!

HONCHO'S PROBABLY FINISHED *FIXING* THEM BY NOW... AND IF HE FINDS OUT WHY WE'RE LATE, HE'LL BE M-MAD!

SO WHO'S GOING TO *TELL* HIM, PIGEON? *YOU...?*

HEY! WHAT **KEPT** YOU GUYS?

IT'S A NICE DAY! WE WENT FOR A WALK!

SO **SUE** US! IT'S **GREAT** BEING ABLE TO GO WHERE WE WANT AFTER THE MONTHS WE SPENT IN THE SLAMMER!

ALL YOU DID WAS **WALK**, HUH? BREATHE IN THE FALL AIR? LISTEN, TURKEYS! I'VE BEEN AROUND! AND SO HAS **SPIDER-MAN!**

WHY DON'T YOU JUST SEND HIM AN ENGRAVED INVITATION ASKING HIM TO ESCORT YOU BACK TO **JAIL!**

S-SEE? I **S-SAID** HE'D BE MAD!

SHUT UP, PIGEON!

SO **SPIDER-MAN** NABBED ME AN' SUGAR FACE FOR MUGGIN'! AND PIGEON HERE FOR PICKIN' SOMEBODY'S POCKET! BIG DEAL!

BEIN' SO ALMIGHTY SMART, MISTER FANCY **ENGINEER**, DIDN'T STOP HIM FROM CATCHIN' YOU PUSHIN' HEROIN!

NO! BUT IT DID PUT ME IN A POSITION TO MAKE FRIENDS WITH THE **VULTURE!**

AND WORKING IN THE MACHINE SHOP LIKE I DID MADE IT REAL EASY TO SMUGGLE SUPPLIES TO HIM...

...AND TALK TO HIM... LOTS!

Y-YEAH! THAT OLD DUDE WAS SO LONELY HE'D TALK TO **ANYBODY!**

PARTICULARLY SOMEONE WHO ADMIRED HIS ENGINEERING GENIUS!

AND WHO HAD THE BRAINS TO USE THE INFORMATION HE'D GIVEN ME... ONCE WE WERE OUT!

WHILE BLOCKS AWAY...

MAY! MAY PARKER!

MARY JANE! WHAT'RE *YOU* DOING HERE?

BUYING A PRESENT FOR THE OSBORNES' NEW BABY! PETE AND I ARE THE GOD PARENTS!

I DIDN'T KNOW! I HADN'T SPOKEN TO MY NEPHEW SINCE WE HAD OUR ARGUMENT!

I'M FURIOUS AT HIM FOR DROPPING HIS GRADUATE STUDIES IN BIO-PHYSICS!

I-I'VE HEARD! BUT MAY, BEING A *PHOTOGRAPHER'S* NO DISGRACE! AND PETE'S GOOD!

LOOK! HIS *SPIDER-MAN* PHOTO'S IN THE BUGLE AGAIN!

SPIDER-MAN IS A MENACE, MARY JANE! I'VE READ THE BUGLE'S EDITORIALS!

I DON'T LIKE PETER TRAIPSING ALL OVER TOWN AFTER HIM! AND THAT'S NOT THE *POINT!* PETER LET HIS *DREAM* DIE!

BUT MAY, WHAT IF HE HAS A *NEW* DREAM? DOES IT MATTER *WHAT* HE DOES AS LONG AS HE'S *HAPPY?*

BUT HE WAS HAPPY BEING A *SCIENTIST!*

AND A PHOTOGRAPHER!

AND *SPIDER-MAN*-- THOUGH I'M THE ONLY ONE WHO KNOWS IT!

THAT ONE'S PERFECT, MAY! *BUY* IT!

MAYBE *LATER*, SWEETIE! I'M HAVING A FEW LITTLE MONEY PROBLEMS WITH THE HOUSE!

NOTHING TO WORRY PETER WITH-- BUT I REALLY CAN'T SPEND THE MONEY RIGHT NOW!

MEANWHILE...

HEY! LET ME GO YOU ALIEN *CREEP!* LET ME--!

WAIT! SURE I'M SCARED! BUT I CAN'T *PANIC!* IT'S THE *PANIC* THAT'S BEATING ME...NOT THE *COSTUME!*

HEY, GET OUTTA HERE, YOU COSTUMED *LUNATIC!* WHAT'RE YOU DOIN' OUT THERE, TWITCHIN' AN' MUMBLIN' TO YOURSELF?

YOU ON DRUGS OR WHAT? I'M WRITIN' THE BUGLE, IT'S A DISGRACE...

SHEESH!

THERE'S *SPIDER-MAN!* HONCHO SAID TO FIND HIM AND--

HEY, WHAT'S *WRONG* WITH HIM, ANYWAY? HE'S JERKIN' 'ROUND LIKE HE'S HAVIN' SOME KIND OF *FIT!*

SLAM!

DON'T ATTACK HIM, HONCHO SAID! JUST SIGNAL THE OTHER *VULTURIONS* WHEN I'VE FOUND HIM!

AN' KEEP MY EYE ON HIM TILL THEY ARRIVE!

DON'T PANIC! STAY CALM! THINK IT THROUGH! ASSESS THE SITUATION! I'M SMARTER THAN IT IS...

I HOPE!

AND I'VE STILL GOT THE PROPORTIONAL SPEED, AGILITY AND STRENGTH OF A SPIDER!

I CAN STILL STICK TO STUFF! ALL MY *INNATE* POWERS ARE INTACT!

EXCEPT MAYBE MY SPIDER SENSE! IF IT WAS WORKING, IT OUGHTA BE SHRIEKING!

WISH I HAD MY WEB SHOOTERS! TOUGH! IF I CAN'T SWING TO THE BAXTER BUILDING, I'LL JUST HAVE TO *WALK* THERE!

THE COSTUME CAN'T STOP ME FROM DOING *THAT!*

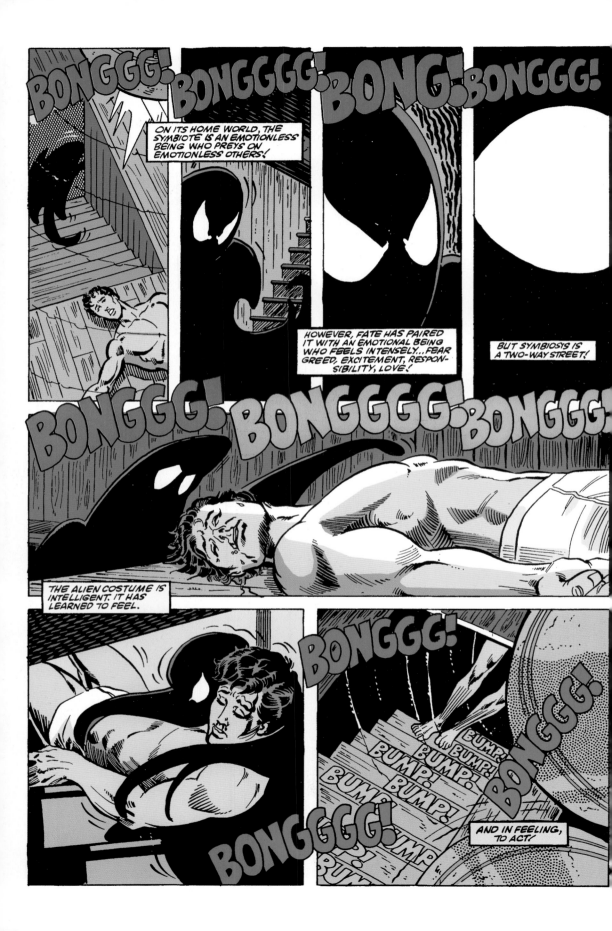

BONGGG!
BONGGGG!

IN A VERY SHORT WHILE PETER PARKER WILL AWAKEN AND WONDER... WHY DID IT SAVE HIM?

IT'S A QUESTION THAT WILL HAUNT HIM FOR THE REST OF HIS LIFE!

FINI.

Finally rid of his parasitic costume, Peter Parker's life returns to normal. Or at least as normal as can be expected for a web-spinning Super Hero. However, Peter is forced to wear a back-up fabric version of his black costume after his original red and blue suit is destroyed in a battle with a villain called Magma.

Tragedy strikes when Police Captain Jean DeWolff, a long-time ally of Spidey's, is killed by a deranged serial killer known as the Sin-Eater. A young reporter called Eddie Brock is given an exclusive interview with a man who claims he is the Sin-Eater. But it is later proved that the man is not the culprit, instead a compulsive confessor, and Brock is fired.

In the following months Peter and Mary Jane continue to rekindle their relationship. Peter eventually proposes to MJ for the second time. She accepts and the two are soon wed. But as the lovebirds get used to their new life as man and wife, new danger looms on the horizon. An unknown stalker begins to shadow Peter Parker's every move. Whilst waiting at a train station, Peter is pushed into the path of an oncoming locomotive. Though his lightning fast reflexes allow him to dodge the train, Peter is more concerned that his unseen assailant was somehow able to evade his spider-sense...

BUT AT THAT MOMENT, ON CHELSEA STREET...

DARN! SHOPPING USUALLY MAKES ME FEEL BETTER--

--BUT I'M STILL ANGRY AT *PETER!* HE'S OUT LATE, PROBABLY OFF BEING SPIDER-MAN, AND HE DIDN'T EVEN LEAVE A MESSAGE ON OUR ANSWERING MACHINE!

I MEAN, I DON'T EXPECT A *MOMENT-BY-MOMENT* ACCOUNT OF HIS WHEREABOUTS--

--BUT A LITTLE *CONSIDERATION* WOULD BE--

--OH! *PETER!*

WHAT WERE YOU DOING SITTING IN THE DARK? NEVER MIND, I'VE GOT A FEW NITS TO PICK WITH--

--PETER? YOUR *BREATHING* SOUNDS FUNNY. ARE YOU ALL--

HI, HONEY...

OH, GOD.

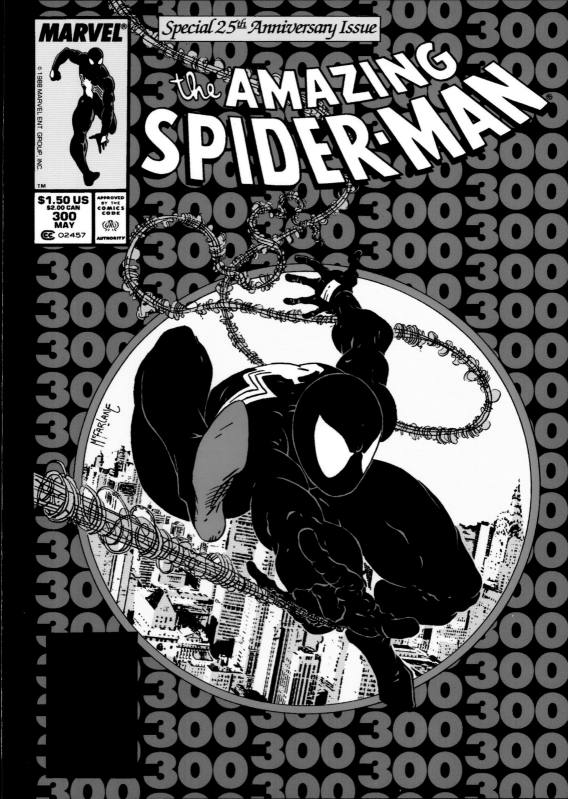

Stan Lee PROUDLY PRESENTS A COMIC BOOK MILESTONE: THE FABULOUS 300TH ISSUE OF...

THE AMAZING SPIDER-MAN®

VENOM

HER NAME IS MARY JANE WATSON-PARKER.

BUT SHE DOESN'T KNOW THAT.

AT THIS MOMENT, SHE KNOWS ALMOST NOTHING.

FOR HER MIND HAS BEEN HARSHLY NUMBED, ALL THOUGHT CRUELLY DROWNED IN AN ONRUSHING TIDE OF PRIMAL FEAR.

AN EMOTION THAT MAY NEVER FULLY FADE...

DON'T COME NEAR ME! P-PLEASE! D-DON'T TOUCH ME!!

DAVID MICHELINIE
WRITER

TODD McFARLANE
ART

RICK PARKER
LETTERS

BOB SHAREN
COLOR

JIM SALICRUP
EDITOR

TOM DeFALCO
EDITOR IN CHIEF

H-HE WORE A COSTUME! BUT HE WAS BIG, B-BULKY... LIKE A WEIGHT-LIFTER! HE WANTED TO KNOW WHERE MY *BOYFRIEND* WAS! HE DIDN'T EVEN KNOW WE WERE MARRIED!

NEVER MIND THAT! ARE *YOU* OKAY? DID HE *HURT* YOU?

BUT WHAT IF HE *IS* LOOKING FOR YOU? H-HE GREW A MOUTH, PETER! RIGHT ON HIS MASK! HE *GREW* IT!

NOT... PHYSICALLY. H-HE JUST MADE ME FEEL SO *HELPLESS.*

H-HE WASN'T *HUMAN...!*

LET'S WORRY ABOUT THAT LATER! RIGHT NOW, I'M GETTING YOU TO A *DOCTOR* AND--

NO! I-I MEAN, I'M OKAY. REALLY. I-IT'S JUST... I CAN'T STAY *HERE* TONIGHT, PETER.

NOT... NOT AFTER...

I UNDERSTAND. I'LL THROW SOME THINGS IN AN OVER-NIGHT BAG AND WE'LL GO TO A HOTEL. YOU JUST TAKE IT EASY.

MARY JANE'S ONE OF THE *STRONGEST* WOMEN I KNOW! BUT SHE'S TREMBLING LIKE A LITTLE GIRL!

WHAT KIND OF MONSTER COULD *DO* THAT TO HER?

NAGEL

MIDNIGHT: THE LYDEN HOUSE HOTEL IN MID-MANHATTAN...

DON'T KNOW WHO THE *MAN* WHO BROKE IN WAS, BUT FROM MJ'S DESCRIPTION, THE INHUMAN *THING* SHE SAW SOUNDS AN AWFUL LOT LIKE--

CAN'T SLEEP. TOO TENSE. THINK I KNOW WHO THAT *INTRUDER* COULD HAVE BEEN. TROUBLE IS--

--MY OLD *COSTUME!*

--THAT'S *IMPOSSIBLE!*

" I FIRST GOT MY BLACK-AND-WHITE SUIT ON ANOTHER PLANET, DURING THAT *BEYONDER* THING.✳ I BROUGHT IT TO EARTH BECAUSE IT WAS GREAT HAVING A COSTUME THAT COULD *MIMIC* MY CIVILIAN CLOTHES, AND CHANGE FROM ONE TO THE OTHER AT A MENTAL COMMAND!

" THE PROBLEMS STARTED WHEN *MR. FANTASTIC* DISCOVERED WHAT MY COSTUME REALLY WAS:

" A LIVING, THINKING, SYMBIOTIC *BEING!* "

✳FOR MORE INFO, SEE *SECRET WARS* #9. -- J.S.

AN ALIEN WHO WANTED ME FOR ITS *HOST*, WHO EVEN TRIED TO *BOND* ITSELF TO MY BODY!

"IT FINALLY TOOK MR. FANTASTIC'S *SONIC BLASTER* TO CAPTURE THE CREATURE!

"BUT IT ESCAPED, DETERMINED TO JOIN WITH ME *PERMANENTLY*. I GOT DESPERATE.

"-- AND LET THE SHATTERING CLAMOR OF THE BELLS *KILL* THE MONSTER BEFORE IT COULD DESTROY *ME!* "*

"*SO* DESPERATE THAT I LURED IT TO A CHURCH TOWER--

*SEE *WEB OF SPIDER-MAN* #1.-- J.S.

BUT FROM WHAT MARY JANE SAYS, THE REPORTS OF THAT DEATH MAY HAVE BEEN SOMEWHAT... *PREMATURE!*

NUTS. I'M REALLY STRUNG TIGHT.

IN THE PAST, I'D LOOSEN UP WITH A LITTLE WEB-SWINGING, MAYBE TAKE SOME PHOTOS FOR THE *DAILY BUGLE.*

BUT I'M A MARRIED MAN NOW, AND I HAVE TO STAY WITH MARY JANE UNTIL--

NNNNNN... PETER?

COME TO BED.

I THINK I KNOW WHO TERRORIZED YOU, MJ. AND WHY THEY'RE AFTER SPIDER-MAN. I HOPED MY HAVING A *SECRET IDENTITY* WOULD SHIELD YOU, BUT--

HUSH, TIGER. WHEN I SIGNED ON "FOR BETTER OR FOR WORSE," I *MEANT* IT.

NOW LET'S GET SOME SLEEP, OKAY?

STUBBORNLY, GRUDGINGLY, FITFUL SLEEP FINALLY COMES.

AND EVENTUALLY, AS THE SUN SLIPS INTO ITS ASSIGNED POSITION OVER MANHATTAN ONCE MORE...

ERRRNGG... ≥YAWN≤ MARY JANE...?

OVER HERE, PETER.

I HOPE YOU WEREN'T CALLING ROOM SERVICE -- I ALREADY KNOW WHAT *I* WANT FOR BREAKFAST!

-- AND WE'VE BEEN MOVED TO THE TOP OF THE WAITING LIST FOR THE *BEDFORD TOWERS!*

IF WE WANT THAT CONDO, IT'S *OURS!*

B-BUT, IT USUALLY TAKES *MONTHS* TO GET A GOOD PLACE IN MANHATTAN!

I GUESS WE WERE JUST LUCKY. I KNOW THIS IS SUDDEN, PETER, BUT I JUST *CAN'T* LIVE IN THAT APARTMENT ANYMORE. I'D SCREAM AT EVERY LITTLE CREAK OR RATTLE!

SILLY. I WAS CALLING A REAL ESTATE AGENT I KNOW. I'VE PULLED IN SOME MARKERS--

YOU DO UNDERSTAND,... DON'T YOU?

IF I HAD A NICKEL FOR EVERY TIME I'VE DROPPED THROUGH THIS SKYLIGHT--

--MAYBE I COULD AFFORD TO PAY FOR MY SHARE OF THAT CONDO!

SPEAKING OF WHICH--

--I WONDER IF THERE'LL BE A PROBLEM GETTING IN AND OUT AS SPIDER-MAN?

GUESS I'LL SWING ACROSS THAT BRIDGE WHEN I COME TO IT. NOW, I'VE GOT OTHER THINGS TO WORRY ABOUT.

AND TO TAKE PRECAUTIONS AGAINST!

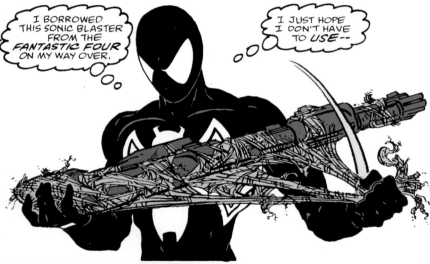

I BORROWED THIS SONIC BLASTER FROM THE FANTASTIC FOUR ON MY WAY OVER.

I JUST HOPE I DON'T HAVE TO USE--

--HNH? LIGHT BLINKING ON MARY JANE'S ANSWERING MACHINE. BETTER SEE WHAT IT IS.

HI, KIDS! THIS IS AUNT MAY. JUST CALLING TO REMIND YOU ABOUT DINNER TONIGHT. CHICKEN AND DUMPLINGS AT SEVEN P.M. SHORT-- I-I MEAN SHARP! OH, PHOOEY, I HATE THESE CONTRAPTIONS! ≶CLICK≶

SONY.

HE'S DUCKING INTO AN ALLEYWAY! MUST BE A SHORT-CUT!

BLAST! NO *CROWD* TO HIDE IN! WE'D BETTER GIVE HIM A FEW SECONDS TO GET AHEAD, THEN--

WHAT--?! HE'S *GONE!*

LIVING IN NEW YORK FOR SO LONG MAY HAVE MADE ME *PARANOID,* BUT I CAN'T HELP BELIEVING THAT OLD SAYING: "BETTER SAFE--

"--THAN *SPLATTERED!*"

AND THUS, A SHORT WHILE LATER, AT THE EXCLUSIVE *BEDFORD TOWERS* CONDOMINIUM RESIDENCE...

WOW.

AND THAT EVENING, AT THE QUEENS COUNTY BOARDING HOUSE OWNED AND RUN BY *MAY PARKER*...

MY, YOU YOUNGSTERS CERTAINLY LOOK *HEALTHY!* MARRIAGE MUST AGREE WITH YOU!

APPARENTLY IT DOES, MAY. THAT *NEPHEW* OF YOURS HAS BEEN IGNORING YOU EVEN *MORE* THAN BEFORE HE GOT HITCHED!

NOW YOU HUSH, NATHAN LUBENSKY! THE CHILDREN HAVE LIVES OF THEIR OWN TO LEAD!

I HOPE YOU'LL FORGIVE MY LITTLE ≥AHEM≤ TIRADE. I'D BETTER GO PUT THESE DISHES IN TO SOAK.

OH, NO, DEAR! YOU STAY WITH PETER, WHERE YOU BELONG.

I'LL HELP.

BACK IN A SEC, HON.

UH-HUH.

YEAH, THAT WAS THE YEAR *LUCKY LINDY* HIMSELF CAME INTO MY SHOP. I REMEMBER--

THOUGH YOU PROBABLY WON'T BELIEVE THAT WE FIND THIS *PARTICULAR* CHOICE RATHER--

--REPULSIVE!

WHA--?!

GHYYAFF!

FLIP

POON!

C-CAN'T... *BREATHE!* S-SU... SUFFOC...

INNOCENT DEATH IS ALWAYS UNPLEASANT.

BUT *NOTHING* MUST STAND IN OUR WAY. NOTHING MUST BLOCK OUR RIGHTEOUS REVENGE! AND BY ALL THAT'S SACRED--

-- NOTHING *WILL!*

AND, EVENTUALLY...

≥WHEW≤ THAT'S THE LAST ONE!

SHOOT. AND I WAS JUST GETTING PUMPED UP!

MAYBE THEY'LL LET YOU CARRY THE *VAN* BACK TO THE *RENTAL AGENCY*, FLASH!

COME AND GET IT!

SANDY AND I'LL BUILD SOME MORE SANDWICHES WHILE YOU GUYS WORK ON THESE. SODAS ARE IN THE FRIDGE.

DIG IN!

GIVE ANY MORE THOUGHT TO MY SUGGESTION, PETE? ABOUT GETTING OUT OF NEWS PHOTOGRAPHY?

YOU'RE THE *BUGLE'S* EDITOR IN CHIEF, ROBBIE-- HOW COULD I *NOT* TAKE YOU SERIOUSLY?

IN FACT, I'VE BEEN THINKING HOW *SCIENCE* USED TO BE MY DRIVING AMBITION. MAYBE--EH?

'SCUSE ME, ROBBIE. THERE'S SOMETHING I HAVE TO DO.

NEED ANY HELP?

NO. I THINK I'D BETTER HANDLE THIS *ALONE*...!

THREE MINUTES LATER, OVER THE SOUTH BRONX...

THAT CREEP MUST'VE CHECKED CHELSEA STREET AND FOUND I WASN'T THERE ANYMORE! NOW HE'S *LOOKING* FOR ME!

AND I COULDN'T TAKE A CHANCE ON HIM *FINDING* ME WITH ALL MY *FRIENDS* AROUND!

I JUST HOPE HE HASN'T GOTTEN SO FAR AHEAD THAT--

--BINGO! CRAWLING INTO THAT ABANDONED BUILDING!

I'LL JUST FOLLOW, SCOPE OUT THE SITUATION, THEN TAKE HIM BY SURPRISE! AFTER ALL--

--MY *SPIDER-SENSE* WILL WARN ME IF THERE'S ANY *DANGER!*

WOM!

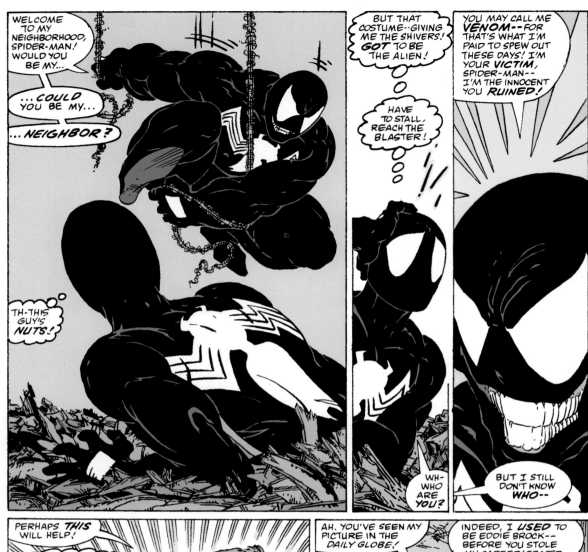

WELCOME TO MY NEIGHBORHOOD, SPIDER-MAN! WOULD YOU BE MY...

...COULD YOU BE MY...

...NEIGHBOR?

TH-THIS GUY'S NUTS!

BUT THAT COSTUME--GIVING ME THE SHIVERS! GOT TO BE THE ALIEN!

HAVE TO STALL, REACH THE BLASTER!

WH-WHO ARE YOU?

YOU MAY CALL ME VENOM--FOR THAT'S WHAT I'M PAID TO SPEW OUT THESE DAYS! I'M YOUR VICTIM, SPIDER-MAN-- I'M THE INNOCENT YOU RUINED!

BUT I STILL DON'T KNOW WHO--

PERHAPS THIS WILL HELP!

MASK FLOWING FROM HIS FACE! LOOKS FAMILIAR! LIKE--≷GASP≶

EDDIE BROCK?!

AH. YOU'VE SEEN MY PICTURE IN THE DAILY GLOBE!

OBLITERATED EVERYTHING I LIVED FOR!

INDEED, I USED TO BE EDDIE BROCK-- BEFORE YOU STOLE MY CAREER! ERASED MY FUTURE!

MY COLUMN IN THE *DAILY GLOBE* WAS READ BY MILLIONS!

I WAS A SOLID REPORTER, A RESPECTED MEMBER OF THE FOURTH ESTATE!

"AT LEAST I WAS WHEN I BEGAN WRITING A SERIES OF ARTICLES ON THE *"SIN-EATER"* MURDERS A FEW MONTHS BACK.

"IT WAS PARTLY BECAUSE OF THOSE ARTICLES THAT I WAS CONTACTED BY A *MR. EMIL GREGG,* A MAN WHO CONFESSED TO *BEING* SIN-EATER!

"PROTECTING MR. GREGG'S IDENTITY THROUGH MY RIGHTS UNDER THE FIRST AMENDMENT,.. I TOLD HIS STORY,.. INCISIVELY, COMPASSIONATELY.

"THE GLOBE'S CIRCULATION SOARED.

"BUT *PRESSURE* ALSO MOUNTED. THE POLICE INSISTED THAT I REVEAL MY SOURCE, SO THAT THEY COULD *STOP* THE MURDER SPREE. UNDER ADVICE OF COUNSEL, I FINALLY WROTE MY MASTERPIECE, ANNOUNCING GREGG AS THE SIN-EATER.*

FINAL THE DAILY GLOBE 30¢
EXCLUSIVE: SIN-EA— REV—

FINAL THE DAILY GLOBE 30¢
EXCLUSIVE: SIN-EATER REVEALED!

"IT WAS A SENSATION--

*THESE EVENTS OCCURRED BETWEEN THE LINES DURING *SPECTACULAR SPIDER-MAN #107-110.-- J.S.*

THAT'S IT... KEEP TALKING!

-- MY LIFE WOULDN'T HAVE BEEN *SHATTERED!* I MAY HAVE MADE AN ERROR IN JUDGMENT, BUT I WAS ALWAYS A *GOOD* JOURNALIST.

AND THE GARBAGE I WAS FORCED TO WRITE BEGAN TO ROT MY SOUL.

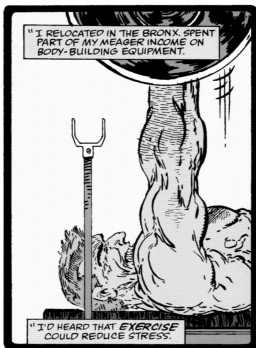

"I RELOCATED IN THE BRONX. SPENT PART OF MY MEAGER INCOME ON BODY-BUILDING EQUIPMENT.

"I'D HEARD THAT *EXERCISE* COULD REDUCE STRESS."

IT DIDN'T WORK.

"WHENEVER I LIFTED A BARBELL, IT *WAS* YOUR *THROAT* I WAS SQUEEZING.

EACH TIME I PUNCHED THE HEAVY BAG, I WAS PULPING YOUR *FACE.*

"I TAPED HEADLINES ABOUT YOU ON MY WALLS, FEEDING MY HATRED, KNOWING THAT *I* COULDN'T GET A STORY EVEN ON THE *BACK PAGE* OF ANY RESPECTABLE PAPER.

"UNTIL, FINALLY, THE PAIN BECAME UNBEARABLE--

ALMOST THERE...!

I THINK I'M IN TROUBLE! ¿OONF!

THE ALIEN WASN'T REALLY *KILLED* BY THOSE BELLS! MUST'VE JUST DISSIPATED OUT OF PAIN! OR... REJECTION!

PROBABLY SENSED BROCK'S DESIRE TO KILL ME, AND THOUGHT THAT WAS A GOOD IDEA--

-- SINCE *I* HAD TRIED TO KILL *IT!*

¿AGH!¿

STILL DON'T KNOW WHY VENOM'S NOT TRIGGERING MY *SPIDER-SENSE,* THOUGH! AND I'M PAYING FOR THAT IGNORANCE IN *PAIN!*

HE'S GOT ALL OF MY POWERS, AND *MORE* MUSCLE! ALL I'VE GOT IS *EXPERIENCE!*

HAVE TO USE STRATEGY! CALL ON MY *CUNNING* TO GET HIM OVER TO THE BLASTER!

≡WHAUGH≡

SO MUCH...

...FOR FINESSE!

WHROK

NOW, YOU SON OF A--!

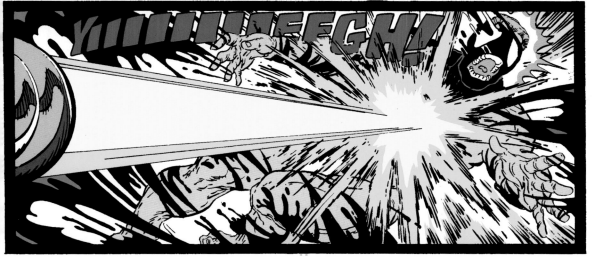

YIIIIIIIIIEEGH!

I DON'T GET IT! WHEN MR. FANTASTIC USED THE BLASTER ON *ME*, THE SYMBIOTE WAS DRIVEN *AWAY!*

BUT IT'S ONLY *PULLING* AWAY FROM BROCK! WHY ISN'T IT *DETACHING?* UNLESS--

--IT *CAN'T?* IT MUST HAVE COMPLETELY *BONDED* WITH HIS BODY! THAT'S WHY HE ISN'T TRIGGERING MY SPIDER-SENSE! THE *ALIEN* NEVER TRIPPED IT--

--AND NOW HE *IS* THE ALIEN!

WHICH MEANS THAT IF I KILL *IT...*

...I'LL KILL *BROCK!*

DON'T KNOW IF I COULD TAKE A *HUMAN* LIFE EVEN TO SAVE MY OWN! AND AFTER THAT BEATING I TOOK, I DON'T HAVE MUCH *FIGHT* LEFT!

I'D BETTER REGROUP, THINK UP A NEW *PLAN--!*

LEAVING?

UH-UH.

PLIP

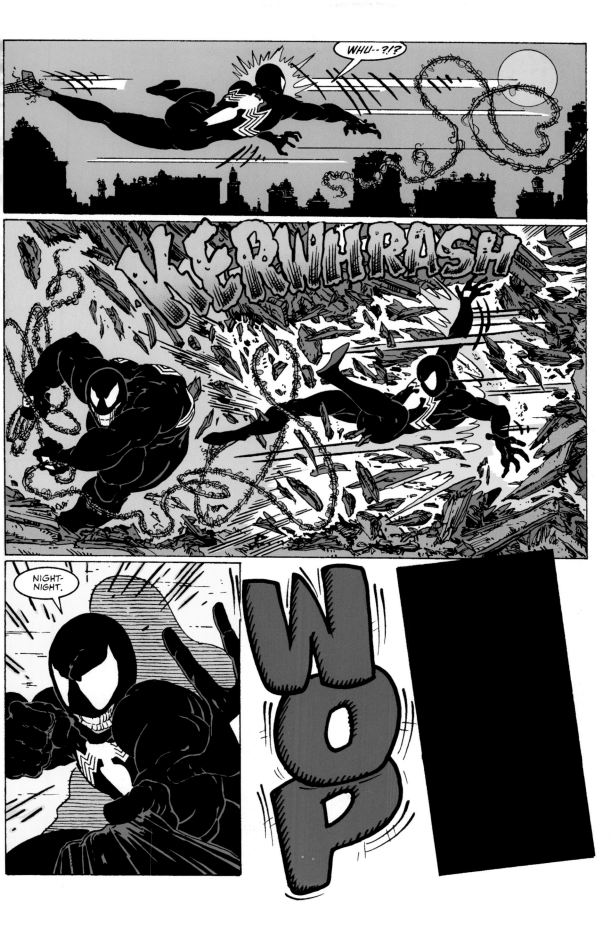

UNKNOWN HOURS PASS.

UUUUUUHH...

WELCOME BACK TO THE LAND OF THE LIVING, SPIDER-MAN! WHAT A PITY YOUR STAY WILL BE SUCH A **SHORT** ONE!

WHA-- **LORD!**

APROPOS SENTIMENTS, CONSIDERING THE CIRCUM-STANCES.

JUST AS MY ALTERED **GARB** IS APPROPRIATE. AFTER ALL, WE ARE, IN A MANNER OF SPEAKING, ABOUT TO EXORCISE--

-- A **DEMON!**

HIH HEEE HA HA HA!

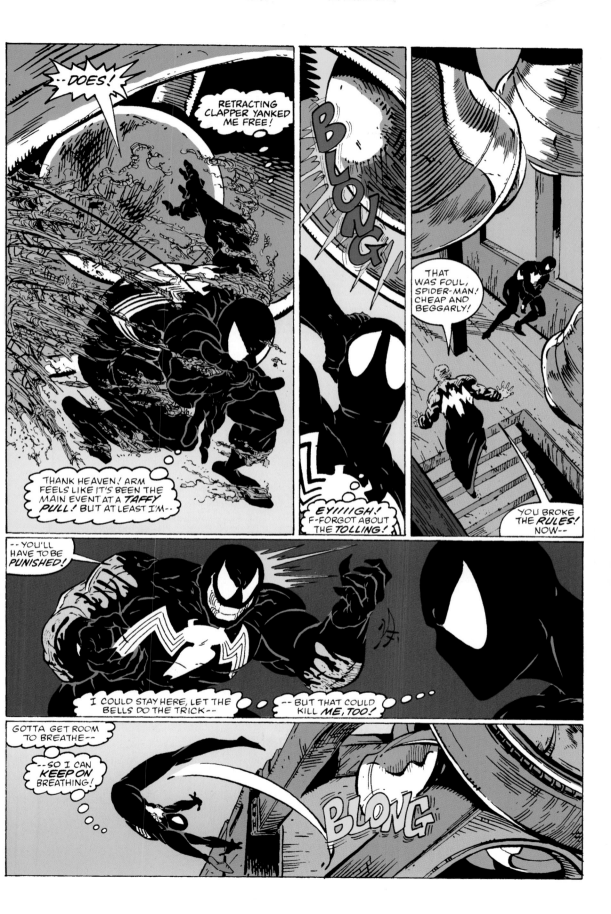

BROCK'S ALIVE--AND SO'S THE ALIEN, THOUGH IT HASN'T REGENERATED ENOUGH OF ITS MASS TO BE A *THREAT* YET.

I'LL NEED TO CONTAIN THEM BOTH, BUT THAT'LL HAVE TO WAIT. NOW--

--IF ONLY I CAN REMEMBER MARY JANE'S *CALLING CARD* NUMBER!

SOON... BEDFORD TOWERS? THIS IS MR. PARKER FROM 8-C. WE JUST MOVED IN AND DON'T HAVE A PHONE YET. COULD YOU POSSIBLY PASS A MESSAGE ALONG TO MY WIFE?

BE MY PLEASURE, SIR. WHAT'S THE GLAD WORD?

JUST TELL HER I HAD TO PHOTO-GRAPH A NEWS STORY, THAT I'LL BE HOME SOON, AND MOST OF ALL...TELL HER I'M *OKAY.*

AND SO, SOME TIME LATER AT *FOUR FREEDOMS PLAZA--*

-- CURRENT TEAM LEADER *BENJAMIN GRIMM* COMPLETES IMPROVISED SECURITY ARRANGE-MENTS...

I'VE BEEN ON THE HORN WITH MR. FANTASTIC, AN' HE SAYS THE *SONICS* BEIN' PIPED INTA THIS CYLINDER SHOULD KEEP *VENOM* NICE AN' DOCILE. LEASTWAYS--

--HOME OF THE LEGENDARY *FANTASTIC FOUR--*

--TILL A SPECIAL CELL CAN BE BUILT FOR 'IM AT *THE VAULT,* THAT GOVERNMENT SUPER-PRISON OUT IN THE ROCKIES!

I REALLY APPRECIATE THIS, BEN.

HEY, NO PROBLEM. ONLY NEXT TIME, TRY TA BRING YER LOONIES IN A LITTLE *EARLIER,* WILL YA? ⸓YAWN⸓

SPIDER-MAN MAKES THE TRIP TO THE BEDFORD TOWERS CAREFULLY, FAVORING HIS LEFT ARM.

AND ONCE THERE, AFTER HIS TALE HAS BEEN TOLD...

WHAT'S WRONG, MJ? YOU SEEM AWFULLY... *DISTANT.*

I *SAID* I WAS SORRY. I DID WHAT I FELT I *HAD* TO DO.

I UNDERSTAND, PETER. REALLY. AND I'M GLAD YOU'RE OKAY.

THEN WHY THE ICEBOX TREATMENT? IS IT BECAUSE I HAVE TO GO RIGHT BACK *OUT* AGAIN?

SWEETHEART, IF I DON'T SHOW UP AT *THE BUGLE* WITH PHOTOGRAPHS OF *SOMETHING* TOMORROW, ROBBIE AND THE OTHERS WILL GET SUSPICIOUS ABOUT WHY I DISAPPEARED FROM THE MOVE PARTY! I HAVE TO--

I *KNOW!*

I... I DIDN'T MEAN TO SNAP AT YOU, PETER. BUT YOU'RE RIGHT-- I *AM* UPSET. ONLY IT'S NOT BE-CAUSE OF YOU. IT'S BECAUSE OF... WELL...

...*THAT!*

AFTER ALL WE'VE BOTH BEEN THROUGH, I DON'T THINK I'LL *EVER* FEEL COMFORTABLE AROUND THAT COSTUME.

YEAH. I KNOW WHAT YOU MEAN.

WEARING THE SAME OUTFIT AS A *HOMICIDAL MANIAC* DOESN'T THRILL ME, EITHER!

AND SINCE IT'S IMPOSSIBLE TO GET VENOM'S SUIT AWAY FROM *HIM*--

--I GUESS I'LL JUST HAVE TO DO WITHOUT *MINE.*

'COURSE, SWINGING AROUND THE CITY IN MY WEB-SHOOTERS AND *FRUIT-OF-THE-LOOMS* ISN'T GOING TO DO WONDERS FOR MY *IMAGE!*

I HAVE AN IDEA ABOUT THAT, PETER.

I KNOW THIS ISN'T A REAL COSTUME, JUST A COMMERCIAL COPY YOU GOT WHEN YOU WERE IN GERMANY. * BUT RIGHT NOW--

--IT ALMOST SEEMS LIKE AN *OLD FRIEND.* WHAT DO YOU THINK?

MARY JANE, I THINK--

*IN THE *SPIDER-MAN* VS. *WOLVERINE* SPECIAL.-- J.S.

--YOU'RE THE GREATEST!

A LINGERING KISS, A QUICK CHANGE OF CLOTHES, AND...

FROM SUIT TO BRUTE...

Did you know that originally **Venom** was going to be a woman? I know it's hard to picture the hulking brute with a jaw that could bite through Wales putting on lipstick, but that was originally the plan.

But let's take a few steps back before that, to the mega-selling Marvel comic book from the mid-eighties, *Secret Wars*. Twelve issues long, it teamed up all the major Marvel superheroes in one big story for the first time. And it began as a toy line.

Toy manufacturer **Mattel** wanted to sell a new toy line based on Marvel superheroes but wanted a big story to accompany them. So Editor-in-Chief of Marvel, **Jim Shooter** offered them a big multi-hero comic series that he would write, featuring everyone from the X-Men to the Fantastic Four, the Hulk to Captain America, and Thor to Iron Man – all fighting villains on an alien planet, far away from home. Lots of scope for playsets, vehicles, and multiple versions of characters.

As part of the story, Jim Shooter wanted all the characters involved to be affected in one way or other before they went back home to their own regular monthly comic books. To make *Secret Wars* really matter.

The previous year, a comics fan had written into Marvel suggesting a story in which Spider-Man got a black costume. Jim Shooter liked the idea so much, he bought it for $220. Editor **Tom DeFalco** worked on the story with the fan, but it didn't come together as a comic. Still, Marvel had paid for the idea. And when Secret Wars came along, Shooter saw his opportunity to bring it back. But rather than a Reed Richards designed black and red armour-like costume, as the fan envisioned, we got something very different.

During the *Secret Wars* series, Spider-man's red and blue uniform had been ripped apart. In a scene plotted by **Roger Stern**, he came across a mysterious alien machine, it created a costume that responded to his mental commands - and in this case, copied the look of *Secret Wars*-co star, Spider-Woman. Designed by **Michael Zeck** and **Rick Leonardi**, everyone was happy with the new look and Spider-Man came back home to show it off to New York.

Of course, it was never going to be that easy, was it?

THE SYMBIOTE REVEALED...

It soon emerged in the Spider-Man comics written by **Tom DeFalco** that the costume was alive. That it was taking Peter Parker out for night time jaunts and leaving him exhausted as a result. The costume was a symbiotic parasite, feeding on him and changing him as a person. So it had to go, thanks to some handy dandy bell tower shenanigans. It turned out the black symbiote costume was allergic to loud noises, to large sonic vibrations. And so that was that. End of the black costume.

Of course it wasn't.

David Michelinie, writer of Amazing Spider-Man planned to bring the symbiote back, attached to another character. The first sign of this was at the end of an issue, when Peter Parker was almost pushed in front of an approaching train by a mysterious unseen woman. That Parker's spider-sense wasn't triggered, was the first clue that something was up. But then Michelinie changed his mind, and went with a male character for the symbiote, Eddie Brock with his own reasons for hating Spider-Man.

But it was emerging comics superstar artist **Todd McFarlane** who would find a way to express this character with greater and greater experimentation, first bulking him up far beyond Eddie Brock's frame, then later adding sharp teeth and an impossibly sized mouth with a snaking tongue to match. And it became a major hit. In Venom we had a character who not only had the same powers as Spider-Man, but who was stronger, faster, knew all his moves, his secret identity, and didn't trigger his spider-sense. Which meant each time they battled Spider-Man had to use his brains, whether finding sonic weapons that would do the trick, or in one famous scene offering himself to the symbiote as a love sacrifice that split Venom in two.

BROCK'S REVENGE

Eddie Brock had written a confession of a super villain, Sin Eater, only for Spider-Man to reveal it wasn't true. Brock, considering suicide, wandered into a church where particles of the black symbiote costume were descending. Finding a common hatred with the discarded costume, who blamed Spider-Man for rejecting it, they became Venom, Together they went after Spider-Man, his family and friends.

THE MONSTER IS LOOSE...

But there was a problem for Marvel. Venom was becoming more and more popular, to the extent that he demanded a series of his own. But how could Marvel give a villain his own book, it would go against the ethos of the publisher. But Venom had always had a moral code about not harming "innocents", so **David Michelinie** upped that a little and turned him into a "lethal protector", a Dexter-like figure who killed the bad guys. Walking the line between the angels and the devils, Venom flipped and flopped from side to side, spawning **Carnage**, another symbiote who was the ultimate in evil, and giving Venom his own bad guy doppleganger to fight. And Spider-Man found himself teaming up with Venom, the creature who had attacked his friends and family, more and more often. Eventually Eddie Brock had enough, and released the symbiote, selling it on for charity.

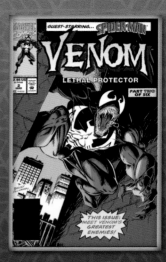

Venom was even in the Spider-Man movie trilogy, as an alien entity that accompanied a crashing meteorite, and went through an initially similar storyline, posessing Peter Parker, and then Eddie Brock, before becoming one of the three big bad guys in the film.

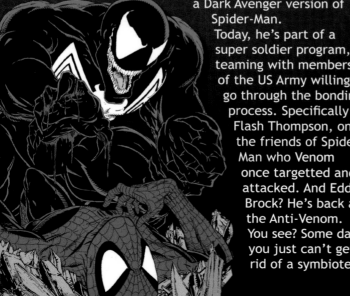

Since then the symbiote has been passed around from bad guy to badder guy, become a government sponsored Venom superhero (with toy) and a Dark Avenger version of Spider-Man.

Today, he's part of a super soldier program, teaming with members of the US Army willing to go through the bonding process. Specifically Flash Thompson, one of the friends of Spider-Man who Venom once targetted and attacked. And Eddie Brock? He's back as the Anti-Venom. You see? Some days you just can't get rid of a symbiote...

THE WRITER

Tom DeFalco

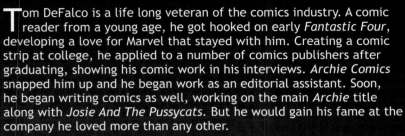

Tom DeFalco is a life long veteran of the comics industry. A comic reader from a young age, he got hooked on early *Fantastic Four*, developing a love for Marvel that stayed with him. Creating a comic strip at college, he applied to a number of comics publishers after graduating, showing his comic work in his interviews. *Archie Comics* snapped him up and he began work as an editorial assistant. Soon, he began writing comics as well, working on the main *Archie* title along with *Josie And The Pussycats*. But he would gain his fame at the company he loved more than any other.

In the late seventies, he joined *Marvel* as a writer, then an editor, staying there for two decades. He launched *Dazzler* in the early eighties, a disco themed superhero comic that was sold exclusively to comic stores - a move that began a major shift in the way comics were sold in America. But it is his Spider-related work for which he is best known. He wrote the *Amazing Spider-Man* series for two years, including the stories that introduced the black costumed Spider-Man to the world, as well as the pre-Venom symbiote storyline that still affects comics to this day.

He also worked with Hasbro on developing both the *GI Joe* and *Transformers* comic, toy line and animated series, as well as writing significant runs of both *Thor* and *Fantastic Four*.

He left *Amazing Spider-Man* on the orders of then-Editor-In-Chief Jim Shooter, but not too long afterwards Shooter himself would be deposed and Tom DeFalco would be made Editor-In-Chief of Marvel, staying in that position from 1987 to 1994.

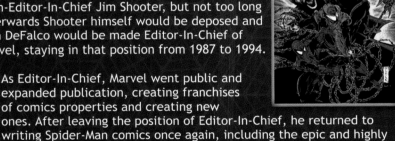

As Editor-In-Chief, Marvel went public and expanded publication, creating franchises of comics properties and creating new ones. After leaving the position of Editor-In-Chief, he returned to writing Spider-Man comics once again, including the epic and highly controversial *Clone Saga*.

He also continued the *Spider-Girl* series, which span out of a *What If--?* issue, looking at the future life of the super powered daughter of Peter Parker and Mary Jane Watson, May. The series survived plenty of cancellation attempts for over a hundred and thirty issues, and became Marvel's longest running solo female comic series.

But when that book finally met its end, DeFalco moved on from Marvel. He published a couple of creator owned comics, returned to Archie to write the spy spoof *The Man From Riverdale*, and most recently went to work at *DC Comics*, working under ex-Marvel colleague Bob Harras on *Superman Beyond*.

Whether Tom DeFalco will return to Marvel is unknown, but the kind of love that he has for the company and characters can only be put off for so long...

ARTIST'S GALLERY
Spider-Man's Costume

The Black Suit saga isn't the only occasion when Spider-Man has changed his iconic red and blue costume. Below are a few of the different suits he has worn during his crime-fighting career.

SCARLET SPIDER

When Peter Parker briefly retired from being Spider-Man, his clone Ben Reilly took on his crime-fighting responsibilities as the Scarlet Spider.

First Appearance:
Web Of Spider-Man #118 (1994)

ELECTRO-PROOF SUIT

This totally insulated suit allowed Spidey to battle a powered-up Electro without fear of being burnt to a crisp.

First Appearance:
Amazing Spider-Man #425 (1997)

THE BOMBASTIC BAG-MAN

When Spidey had a million dollar bounty placed on his head, he had to find a new disguise in order to safely swing around town. A quick spot of improvisation led to the creation of the Bombastic Bag Man!

First Appearance: Spectacular Spider-Man #256 (1998)

CAPTAIN UNIVERSE

Possessed by an alien energy called the Enigma Force, Spider-Man was briefly transformed into the cosmic-powered hero Captain Universe.

First Appearance: Spectacular Spider-Man #158 (1989)

IRON SPIDER

Created by Tony Stark, this hi-tech suit featured cutting edge technology, including three mechanical arms that Spidey could control with his mind.

First Appearance: Amazing Spider-Man #529 (2006)

ARMOURED SPIDER-MAN

In order to defeat a heavily armed group of criminals called the Enforcers, Peter created a new bullet-proof Spidey suit.

First Appearance: Web Of Spider-Man #100 (1993)

FURTHER READING

If you've enjoyed the style and art in this graphic novel, you may be interested in exploring some of these books too.

Spider-Man: Blue

Volume 25 of the Ultimate Marvel Graphic Novels Collection

At the book shop:
ISBN: 9780785110712

Spider-Man: Origin Of The Hobgoblin

At the book shop:
ISBN:9780785158547

Spider-Man: Kraven's Last Hunt

Volume 10 of the Ultimate Marvel Graphic Novels Collection

At the book shop:
ISBN: 9780785134503

Amazing Spider-Girl: Whatever Happened To The Daughter of Spider-Man?

At the book shop:
ISBN: 9780785123415

The Mighty Thor: The Last Viking

Volume 5 of the Ultimate Marvel Graphic Novels Collection

At the book shop:
ISBN: 9780785131892

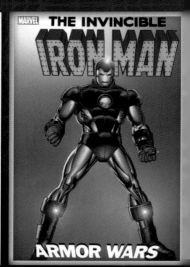

Iron Man: Armor Wars

At the book shop:
ISBN: 9780785125068